COMMUNITY ACTION

A Place Like Home

A Radical Experiment in Health Care

Gillian Wilce has worked as a social worker in the borough of Southwark, as a secretary and as an editor, including five years as Literary Editor of the *New Statesman*. She is now a freelance editor and part-time medical research assistant.

She lived in the North Lambeth area for 17 years, and now lives in Islington.

A Place Like Home

A Radical Experiment in Health Care

Gillian Wilce

Bedford Square Press

Published by
Bedford Square Press of the
National Council for Voluntary Organisations
26 Bedford Square, London WC1B 3MU

First published 1988

© Lambeth Community Care Centre, 1988

ISBN 0 7199 1228 8

Typeset by Saxon Graphic Services Ltd
Printed and bound in England by Latimer Trend & Co Ltd, Plymouth

A CIP catalogue record for this book is available from the British Library.

Contents

Foreword

Speech delivered by HRH The Prince of Wales at the opening of Lambeth Community Care Centre on 20 November 1985.

I have been asked to say a few words just to declare open this new community health centre, and I really am delighted that both my wife and myself are able to be here for this rather special occasion. The only trouble is I'm very sad in a way that it had to be in November and not in July, when it would have been considerably nicer for all of you. Not only that, but we would have been able to see this particular building probably looking its best, with all the light and the shade and the sun coming through this conservatory here. I hope in the years to come we shall be able to come back and see it as it really should be in the summer.

I have heard a great deal about this particular centre, and I know it will provide a very important primary care service which is, as you know, a most essential element in the health services that we have in this country. It is more than anything else of course in between the home and hospital, and from that point of view provides a particularly essential personal service rather than the sometimes impersonal services that you might get in a larger hospital. I think that many people would agree that a district general hospital has specialist beds which are not always applicable to the needs of many patients who will come here and use this particular centre.

I am reliably informed that the building pleases almost everyone, which is a remarkable state of affairs if it is in fact true, and that more than anything else this building is seen as belonging to everybody in the locality. Apart from anything else it has been designed from the point of view of therapeutic architecture, with which I am in total and utter agreement.

The garden, as I've just discovered, is a very important feature in the design of the whole place, and I know that the tree planting is a very important feature as well. I am delighted to have been able to bring my own tree to plant for the first time ever. I shall look forward to seeing it flourish and also to provide with a bit of luck a roosting place for the odd owl; it would have to be a very odd owl here I think!

But ladies and gentlemen, this concept here is a rediscovery more than anything else of Florence Nightingale's belief in what she described as a physic for the mind as well as the body. Everything in the 1960s tended to be jettisoned in favour of a different approach, but now I think people are realising that the kind of approach we have here is probably more relevant, where the patients and everybody else, the doctors, and the inter-disciplinary staff, are all asked for their views on what they would like to have.

The building itself is described as a country house for the inner city in an arts and crafts prairie style. It always intrigues me the descriptions that people give these particular designs. I'm sure that is exactly what it is, but I do hope and pray that all those who come here and receive treatment of one kind or another will find it more than anything else to be a real place of healing. This is what it has been designed for, as a healing centre in the old and traditional sense of the word.

On that note it gives me enormous pleasure to declare this building well and truly open.

Introduction

One snowy winter evening in 1987, in the women's changing room at the Lambeth Community Care Centre, while nurses and therapists manoeuvred round one another, discarding work dresses in favour of sweaters, scarves and boots, talk turned to where they would most want to be if they were ill themselves. Like a single chorus with several voices, they admitted to a communal fantasy of finding, by hook or by crook, an address within the Centre's area since, of all the places in which they had been employed, this was the one in which they would prefer to be ill.

This book is an attempt to explain what the Community Care Centre is, why it is not only — I think — unique but offers an example to be carefully considered by anyone concerned about our health service or, indeed, about health at all: an example of medically skilled provision which is particularly appropriate to the needs of this inner-city area because it grew out of a long preparatory period of listening to the people of the neighbourhood; an example of small-scale, local, intermediate and relatively inexpensive health care; an example of an ambience in which patients feel still connected with their daily lives; an example of genuine partnership, with patients being equal participants in their own health care rather than mere subjects of medical attention; an example, too, of beginning to involve local communities as a whole in their own future health, a health which is perceived as intimately related to other aspects of society.

Introducing a special issue about the new Centre, the *Architects' Journal* (16 October 1985) spoke of it as:

> our hope for a National Health Service Mark II, an
> important evolution of what is left of the civilised values
> which gave birth to the currently threatened post-war NHS
> Mark I . . . a continuation of that fine inter-war libertarian
> tradition where local community health pioneers, together
> with architects, transformed their separate, and then finally
> shared, visions of hope into reality.

This account will start with a brief description of the Centre's
genesis and will then consider the working out of its philosophy
in practice. I have used first-person pronouns for my own
reactions because I have no desire to lay claim to a spurious
objectivity. This is not the work of a researcher or a health
economist; it is simply a recounting of what was seen and heard
during a couple of months around the Centre. It also incor-
porates stories that some staff and GPs wrote down after the
Centre had been going for a year, stories which seemed to them
to illuminate its unique contribution.

I have chosen not to name anyone in the text. That was
originally in order not to have to distinguish between people who
were happy to be identified and those who would prefer not to
be. In the event, that the book should be free of names feels true
to the nature of the place. While wholly predicated on the value
of individuals, the Centre nevertheless has an importance
beyond the particular group of people involved at any one time.
That acknowledged, though, I would like to say as emphatically
as possible that, while mistakes in interpretation are all my own
and my account is bound to be partial and limited, any life this
book has comes from the following people who either talked to
me or allowed me to use what they had written and who are all
quoted directly, some of them at considerable length, in the text:
Dr John Balasz, Dr Steven Curson, Charles Daubney (patient),
Shamsher Diu (dentist), Jenny Douglas (administrator),
Dr Frances Dudley, Penny Fergusson (sister), Dr Esther Fonseca,
Sue Freudenberg (member of project team/ex-CHC secretary),
Dr Roger Higgs, Dr Stewart Kay, Dr Jennifer Law, Dr Sir
Montague Levine, Dr Bill Marson, Professor Dr David Morrell,
Margaret Neville (patient), Lesley Nixon (community link
worker), Dr Jennifer Pietroni, Dr Raymond Pietroni, Dr David
Poole, Helen Ruddock-West (senior occupational therapist),

Martin Smit (senior nurse research, West Lambeth Health Authority), Jane Sparrow (sister), Jo West (senior physiotherapist), Sheila Woodward (senior nurse) and Dr Luke Zander. They, together with all the other members of staff and patients whose remarks at meetings and in casual conversations have contributed to a picture of the Centre in action, are the true authors of the substance of this account.

Publisher's acknowledgement

The publishers are grateful to the King Edward's Hospital Fund for London for generously providing a grant to help subsidise the production costs of this book.

1 Beginnings

> It's been so well thought out. If our sheltered housing and this centre is what Lambeth can do then Lambeth suits me. I just hope that in due course they can build other Centres like this dotted all around.
>
> (Voluntary helper)

If, from the middle of London, you go by Northern or Bakerloo Line to the Elephant & Castle, negotiate a graffiti-splattered underpass into Newington Butts, take the path beside the newish leisure centre, skirt the tourist hotel and go past the temporary post-war prefabs (still inhabited), you'll find yourself in Brook Drive, SE11. It runs between three-and four-storey terraced houses straight down to the Kennington Road, coming out beside the Imperial War Museum opposite the 1930s' China Walk Estate.

On the right-hand pavement you would be in the Borough of Southwark but on the left-hand side you're entering Lambeth. And just beyond the 'Welcome to Lambeth: a nuclear free zone' sign, with its local comment in the form of a crudely over-sprayed red hammer and sickle, is the dark bulk of the Lambeth Hospital, a busy general hospital from the beginning of the century until the 1970s but closed and silent now.

Genesis
In the early 1960s, when there was a fashion for large-scale, centralised solutions to problems, the Ministry of Health published a *Hospital Plan for England and Wales*, recommending

concentrating medical services in big units and closing smaller hospitals. The Lambeth (as it was commonly known) was not only part of St Thomas' (just a brisk 15 minutes' walk away), but also within easy reach of two other major teaching hospitals. So it was not surprising that, in 1974, the local health district proposed its closure.

However, community health councils had come into being the previous year in order to act on behalf of the 'consumers' of health services and in 1974 the new Labour Minister of Health David Owen gave them further powers, including a right to be consulted before any hospital was closed.

So, the St Thomas' Community Health Council (later renamed the West Lambeth CHC) received notice of a proposal to close the Lambeth Hospital, transfer its patients to St Thomas' and make use of the nine-acre site for ancillary services. The response of the CHC was that it would not oppose the closure *if* the site could truly be used *for* the local community.

The CHC's next step was to devote itself for quite some time to finding out what people in the area wanted of their health services. Through the Elephant & Castle, bits of the Borough and Waterloo, along the edge of the Thames through North Lambeth to Vauxhall, round through the Oval and back, via Walworth Road, to the Elephant again, in an area of balconied thirties' LCC estates and high-rise sixties' council blocks, of Peabody and Guinness Trust flats, of old terraces and a few small enclaves of owner-occupied Georgian, CHC members talked with over 100 local groups of all kinds. They held public meetings, advertised through tenants' and residents' associations, and sought out the views of special interest groups like the elderly or mothers with small children. On one estate they carried out a survey of one in five households. They also approached every GP practice in the area, talked to district nurses and health visitors and home helps and social services.

Meantime, David Owen was advocating the usefulness of smaller hospitals. Its 1962 plan having been strongly opposed in many areas — particularly where people had been used to the presence of a cottage hospital, the DHSS, too, had turned to a cautious support for general practitioner hospitals.

Throughout its history, from the early 19th century to the present, the GP or cottage hospital has been considered particularly suitable for rural areas, for secondary centres of population geographically distant from the nearest district general hospital. But what all the CHC's investigations were uncovering was a need, right here in the inner-city, within the sound of Big Ben, under the shadow of several great teaching hospitals, for medical care somewhere between the specialist resources offered by the large hospital and what can be achieved by the primary health services in patients' own homes.

As one of the GPs involved in planning for the Lambeth Hospital site has written,

> In spite of islands of affluence, the predominant medical issues in the inner city are those concerned with impoverishment . . . The problems are well known but worth restating. Housing stock is either old, with families or groups crowded into unsuitably converted buildings with shared facilities, or more modern high-rise which isolates single-parent families or elderly on high floors . . . Many householders are single or live alone . . . isolation is compounded by declining standards of public transport and fear of street violence. Earnings are low. Expenditure is high . . . Health statistics reflect these problems. Accidents, serious respiratory disease, suicide and mental illness are common . . . The immobile elderly become ill unnoticed and alone . . .
> This background helps to define the aim of inner-city community hospitals. There is no competition with specialist units or justification of distance for providing any alternative care in, for instance, obstetrics . . . Likewise, accident work and surgery beyond the scope of the practice belong to the DGH [District General Hospital]. The role for community hospitals here is in the immediate aftercare and rehabilitation of orthopaedic and surgical cases, young and old, relieving pressure on precious acute beds. Likewise, acute medical problems, such as chest infections or strokes, which are well within the general practitioner's medical skills need no longer take up specialist beds for lack of 24-hour home nursing. Terminal care of malignant and non-malignant conditions need no longer fall between local specialist units and the more distant hospice. Pressure

on geriatric and long-stay beds may be relieved by careful
rotation schemes between home and community hospital.
(*Directory of General Practitioner Hospitals, 1983*)

Once the idea of a community hospital had crystallised as the
CHC's vision for the future of the Lambeth site, a project group
was set up to work in more detail on plans and to negotiate as
necessary with other bodies about those plans. This group
included four enthusiastic GPs from four different practices
(though it has to be acknowledged that initial enthusiasm was
not universal; other local GPs were uncommitted, indifferent or
even sceptical at first, being drawn in one by one for different
reasons at different stages over the next eight years). The group
also included the then CHC secretary (a prime mover of the
project), CHC members, representatives of the community
nursing services, occupational therapists (OTs) and St Thomas'
planning department.

This was when the hard slog really began. All the project
group members were passionately committed to the concept of a
community hospital, cared a lot about getting it right and spent
an immense amount of time and energy doing so. As well as
regular meetings, outings to view related projects and protracted
discussions about proposals and procedures, there was the long,
often embattled process of negotiating with the powers-that-be,
explaining themselves, coping with rejections, moderating plans
while sticking by their essential vision in what the GP quoted
above described as the 'long process of proposal, modification,
application and re-application to the [then] three-layered health
service'.

The history of the group's work is almost a whole story on its
own. The driving energy of the CHC secretary is often said to
have provided the decisive momentum, while she pays tribute to
the persistent commitment of busy GPs through years of seeing
no apparent results. And everyone agrees that the presence of a
member of St Thomas' planning department, and the particular
contribution of that particular member, was vitally important.
Local groups and Lambeth Borough, with its continued interest
as planning authority in the future of the site, are also credited
with providing valuable support. The groups who backed the
project are as various as Lambeth Inner Cities Consultative
Group, King's Community Health Council, North Lambeth

Neighbourhood Council, the Vauxhall Society, Hayles' Tenants' Association, Cottington Estate Residents' Association, Kennington Estates Residents' Association, Stockwell and Vauxhall Neighbourhood Council, Lambeth Age Concern and Lambeth Trades Council as well as a great many neighbourhood groups belonging to the Association of Waterloo Groups.

When, after years of persistence by the project team, the District Management Team eventually issued its imprimatur, it was with one small proviso — that the team find the money for the Centre themselves. Negotiations with the Inner City Partnership resulted in the offer of capital funding and money for running costs for 18 months (for a medical project the Partnership will offer 100 per cent funding; with other projects ICP money has to be matched with other funds).

Then there was the necessity to find architects who would work in partnership with the project team, sharing their vision and translating it into architectural form.

'The project has been fortunate indeed,' a GP commented later on the firm of Cullinans,

> to find architects who provided an intuitive and brilliantly intelligent response, and who helped the project group to define its concepts and procedures as well as establishing building requirements. For many members of the project team, subjecting one's professional aims and attitudes to shared scrutiny was an uncomfortable experience, but the rewards were great, and the enthusiasm generated created original thinking in both health care and architecture.

The first detailed plan was produced in the autumn of 1981 — not, as some of the project group had hankered for, a courtyard arrangement (out of keeping, the architects thought, with a small London street of terraced houses), but a long, low building with a street frontage and garden behind. The final design was agreed in February 1983, the outcome, said Jules Lubbock, architecture critic of the *New Statesman,* writing in the *Architects' Journal,* 'of the tension between the architect's and the client's visions' — an 'inspired, sometimes angry, dedicated and argumentative client' working with architects who 'believe in the art of architecture'. Tenders were invited and the work

began in September 1983. Twenty months later the building was
ready — downstairs day unit and treatment rooms, upstairs ward
and conservatory spiralling between them.

Meantime, there were the details of working practice to be
thrashed out and crucial convictions about health care to be
embodied in words so that they should never be forgotten in the
rush of daily work. The staffing establishment was worked out
and appointments made. A management structure was devised
which would support the Centre while reflecting the hope that it
should itself be a little area of real democracy. Statements of
operational policy were drafted, GPs' exact obligations defined,
admissions procedures sorted out, guidelines agreed and finally,
in May 1985, the project group produced a final 'statement of
purpose', a summary of the aspirations and intentions that had
motivated their 10-year struggle.

> The Centre exists to provide a new type of care and
> rehabilitation for local patients at a level intermediate
> between home and hospital . . .
> Its facilities are aimed at fostering the integration of local
> caring services including health, local authority and
> voluntary sectors . . .
> A multi-disciplinary approach will be emphasised . . .
> The Centre will provide facilities for the rehabilitation of
> patients on a daily basis; for the care of patients who are
> unable to be cared for at home but who do not need to be
> admitted nor to remain in the district general hospital; for
> meetings of primary care staff; and for local community
> activities and meetings concerning health matters . . .
> Staff will consider the Centre to be the patient's home for
> the duration of their stay . . .
> Patients will be given the leading role in defining their
> individual relations with Centre staff . . .
> Treatment plans will be geared to maximising the potential
> activity of the patient following discharge from the
> Centre . . .
> The explicit aim of work in the Centre will be to maintain
> the patient's own freedom to make his/her own decisions
> about treatment and activity whilst in the Centre, acting
> on the advice of staff . . .

The expectations are that patients and their next of kin will always be told the truth about diagnosis, proposed care and prognosis . . .

Opening

In July 1985, just around the corner from the old Lambeth, the new Lambeth Community Care Centre stood ready for its first patients, a low, sunny building with a yellow-edged ambulance bay jutting expectantly towards the street.

Though 10 of the 20 beds and some of the day places were in use from the summer, the ceremonial opening came later in the autumn. Out-patients developed a pressing need to have their appointments on 20 November, in-patients became surprisingly reluctant to get better and go home. The projected visit of Prince Charles and Princess Diana to open the Centre was a big event locally.

And a big event not just in prospect but in fact, too. The Prince and Princess were universally praised afterwards for the ease, knowledgeability and sympathetic interest with which they talked to all the patients and many of the staff.

This is how one patient saw the occasion:

> I had been detailed to ride the exercise bicycle. I found a comfortable chair nearby in a warm corner by a window with a view of the garden. Outside it was cold and threatening snow. The invited guests had to wait outside in the garden until the Royals had toured the Centre. From my warm vantage point I spotted, *inter alia*, several neighbours as well as the top brass, male and female, of the London Ambulance Service in resplendent uniforms . . .
>
> Punctually at 3.15 pm the Royals arrived. Half an hour later they reached my physiotherapy room. The Prince turned right, the Princess left. This meant that I was no. 3 on her tour. She sat down and talked to nos. 1 and 2. I was perched on my bicycle. I was introduced. We shook hands. To her questions I described my various exercises, the symptoms of my stroke and stage of my recovery. I managed to express my thanks to the Centre and to the physiotherapists, the least I could do . . .
>
> It was dark when the tour ended. The Prince planted a

tree in the garden (under floodlights), made a short speech declaring the Centre well and truly opened (the public-address system was first-class), there was a signing of the Visitors Book and punctually at 5 pm the Royals departed to the strains of a steel band which rather drowned the cheers.

And so, after a summer running-in period, it was declared officially open, this project which, its progenitors said, had 'parents and cousins but no siblings'. Unlike most rural GP hospitals, it does not offer casualty services, surgery, maternity care, X-ray or consultant out-patient clinics. Unlike the new purpose-built unit at Wallingford which has twice as many beds for long-stay patients as for short-term treatment, it offers no long-stay facilities at all. And unlike London's other GP hospital, which opened at Chepstow Lodge in Paddington in 1982, it does not concentrate exclusively on in-patients.

So what does the Lambeth Community Care Centre con-tribute? For in-patients, medical care for those conditions, like acute chest infections, which cannot easily be nursed at home but don't need the general hospital's array of specialist services; rehabilitative care after surgery or intensive treatment; terminal care for the dying; respite care for people who can just about keep going independently given the occasional rest, or for people whose carers — husbands, wives, children, siblings, in-laws, friends or neighbours — need a break from time to time.

The day unit provides out-patient facilities for appointments with physiotherapists, occupational therapists, chiropodist, dentist, speech therapist or dietician as well as 35 day places for people who are not quite ready to spend 24 hours a day seven days a week unsupported and need some rehabilitative nursing care. This can range in its scope from changing dressings to counselling or social skills training.

The only doctors directly involved with the Centre are the contracted GPs, 26 of them in the early days, 40 or more now. GPs refer and discharge their own patients and treat them while they are in the Centre. If the GP is off-duty when one of her/his patients in the Centre needs a visit, then the call has to be covered by a named deputy. This means in effect that, whatever a GP may do in other circumstances, she or he may never use a relief service to cover work within the Centre.

But the most important distinguishing feature of the Centre is that it is equipped not just with a new building and set of services but with a coherent philosophy, a conviction that the patient should be enabled to share in his/her own health care as part of a multi-disciplinary team.

This is in harmony with one World Health Organisation definition of primary health care as:

> essential health care made universally acceptable to individuals and families in the community *through their full participation*. It forms an integral part of both the country's health system . . . and of the overall social and economic development of the community [my italics].

Its founders envisaged the Lambeth Community Care Centre as an essential node in just such a system of linkages between health and society. They hoped it would become a meeting place for patients and medical professionals, for people with differing medical and social skills and perspectives, for the health service and the community it serves.

The place itself

This was the vision that had been painstakingly explained to the architects. The result was a building so striking that almost an entire issue of the *Architects' Journal* was dedicated to it, with articles by Peter Buchanan (deputy editor of the *Architectural Review*) and John Ashton (senior lecturer in community health at the University of Liverpool Medical School) as well as by Jules Lubbock. They examine the history and detail of the building as well as the scope and aims of the project housed in it. They are critical in places — Peter Buchanan has negative reactions to some aspects of the design and John Ashton worries about how far it will manage to be truly a part of the community — but the bulk of the comment is enthusiastic and the wealth of detailed description given there cannot be matched here.

Jules Lubbock says in his article that he learnt from talking to some of the Centre's first patients that:

> the building not only assists therapy but is therapeutic in itself. Ward patients ask for the curtains to be opened, look

out at the trees and want to get out of bed. Its beauty and intricacy teases one to explore and encourages patients to walk and become independent . . .

The building also supports patients. There is none of the depersonalisation of waiting in dreary corridors. Waiting is a positive social activity. People talked of 'feeling safe here', they said that the dado rails were 'made for me' (which they weren't), they can rest in the octagons, the poles in the corridors make it easy for the blind to find their way, which was not the intention, and the busy colourful conduits and ceiling plaques make painfully slow journeys a jolly experience [Peter Buchanan found them more of an irritant, a distraction].

Yet not everyone wants to be stimulated all the time. Some patients told me that it was easy to find peace and quiet as well.

And that is one of the things that has most struck me about the Centre — the combination of tranquillity and stimulation which allows you somehow to choose what you most need at that moment. It has, I think, something to do with the light and something to do with the relationship between the spaces within the building. It's an impressive blend for a really rather small building which has to help the sick back into action at the same time as providing a space in which a dying person can be at peace.

'Too bloody beautiful', one early patient thought for it to be possible that he was still in Monkton Street, SE11 (not that there's anything wrong with Monkton Street; it's just an ordinary little London street and the Centre, set within it, manages to look both rather modest and outstandingly different).

One or two small unforeseen snags have come to light with use, like the entrance doors being too heavy to be pushed open by anyone very frail or using a stick or walking frame. (There is, in fact, to be an architectural review by outside experts to consider the whole effectiveness of the building in action.) Such faults as I've heard mentioned are, however, tiny compared with the pleasure and pride that staff and patients take in their building. A small staff arts committee exists in large part to cherish and further enhance the building. There's talk of commissioning a sculpture for the garden, for instance, and in May 1987 they unveiled a series of paintings done by Tom Phillips especially for the Centre's ward.

There's also a garden committee with representatives of the immediate neighbourhood on it. The grass-cutting is contracted out but all the other gardening work is done by volunteers. At a large planting picnic in June 1986 people from the area — and others from further afield who'd developed an affection for the Centre — came bearing plants which they put in themselves, recording in the Visitors Book who'd put what where.

The early degree of concern about the garden may have led one of the architectural critics to comment wrily on the project team's apparent desire for a mini-Sissinghurst in their small plot, but it was worth spending time on. The fight against flat lawns was won and the land slopes and hummocks away from the Centre. The combination of trees, garden, conservatory and verandah with its troughs of bright flowers has undoubtedly proved therapeutic. The sitting area within the conservatory at ward level, a wonderfully light-filled place even on a dark winter afternoon, has proved very popular. Patients use it to talk with their relatives or with their doctor or just to sit quietly. One man who came in for respite care (he had dysarthia [difficulty with speech], ataxia [difficulty with movement] and paralysis of the left side following a stroke) used to set up his easel and paint there, 'a colourful occupant of the "greenhouse"'.

At the end of the building's first year in use, staff and some GPs recorded impressions and experiences of the Centre's early days. One GP reminds us of the needs of the area and describes the quality of the Centre's response to that need. It is not a direct comment on the building and yet it seems to me to reflect what the building also reflects:

> The bulk of the population is drawn from social classes IV and V and the area is characterised by the usual deprivation found in the inner-city, namely poor housing, poor amenities, poor schools, vandalism, violence and, sadly, a deteriorating quality of hospital care. In this practice we have always tried to take a broader view of our patients' problems and the availability of the CCC with its rich

resources and warm approach has made a tremendous impact on those relatively few of our patients who have had the privilege to be treated there. By expanding the nature of the work that we are able to do for our patients it has provided a much needed fillip to our morale and self-esteem.

Another GP, talking on a television programme, spoke of the extraordinary value to users of the Centre of feeling that, at a time of general cutbacks and neglect, something new and carefully wrought had been made for them; that they mattered enough. Several of the GPs referred, as did Jules Lubbock, to the Centre as a place where patients said that they felt safe, 'a safe place to be sent to', 'a sense of safety'. The building is only part of it, but it is an integral part, helping not hindering.

Two children were overheard discussing it one open day. 'I should like to live here,' said one and the other, sagely, 'and I should like to die here'. And that's what the project group had been hoping to create: a place, like home, for living — and for dying — but not for the state of suspended animation that can so easily come about in hospital.

2 Patient Power

It might be argued that if the CCC did not exist, life would inevitably go on for all our patients, but in the final analysis I must say with all the sincerity at my command that I have no doubt whatsoever that the quality of life for very many of my patients has been greatly improved at the time when it was most needed.

(A GP)

Early in 1987 the carousel in the office/reception area housed over 1,700 files. This means that more than 1,700 people had been treated at the Centre during its first 18 months. Many of them came for maybe a couple of out-patient appointments with a physiotherapist but, between July 1985 and June 1986, 316 of them were in-patients. This, remembering that all 20 beds became available only in the second half of the year, means a bed occupancy rate in early days of 81 per cent and that's high. These days it's much more often a case of where to fit in the 21st bed.

Back on her feet
The story of Miss A illustrates some of the ways in which the Centre's insistence on supporting the patient's own autonomy works out in practice.

Miss A lives alone and had gradually since retirement, in her own words, 'let herself go'. She lay all day and night in one room — the sitting-room because it was the only really warm place to be in the cold winter of 1986. She had become considerably overweight and was afflicted with leg ulcers (a nasty but all too common problem among older people).

She had difficulty getting about and when she fell awkwardly one evening on the internal steps in her flat she was unable to get up. At least this was in March, not the coldest part of the winter, and in the morning she was able to attract a neighbour's attention. Although her flat is only on the first floor, the stairs are narrow and steep and the ambulance men had a terrible job getting Miss A down them. She was taken to the nearest general hospital where she had an operation on her dislocated shoulder (her left arm, she says, still doesn't work properly) and where she then lay immobile for five months, her legs being too swollen and ulcerated to walk on. She had a bed which she describes as looking like a boat and being composed of granules constantly shifting to guard against further sores. It began to seem as if she might never walk again. When it was clear that the general hospital could do no more by way of treatment, her GP called in the Community Care Centre and the senior nurse, physio, OT and GP went to the hospital together to see Miss A and to talk to the people who'd been looking after her.

Admission from the hospital to the Centre followed in August 1986 with the quite specific aim of getting Miss A literally back on her feet. Because this was obviously not a short-term project, the admission was carefully planned to breach the Centre's length-of-stay guideline. Normally, 28 days is considered to be the limit, a safeguard against allowing people to stay on and on without any definite treatment programme or plan for future care in view.

There was some doubt about the feasibility of the undertaking to enable Miss A to go back to her own home, not least on the part of Miss A herself who was, unsurprisingly after months on her back, very demoralised. Asked now about the difference between the teaching hospital and the Centre, she has no criticism to make of the care in the former; it was, it seems, almost too good. You stayed in bed and were looked after, she said. At the Centre, she went on somewhat ruefully, they make you 'do for yourself'. Of course they help you as long as you can't manage; they don't just leave you floundering. And at first she did, indeed, have almost everything done for her — was tended and bathed and lifted. But bit by bit she was gently bullied on to her feet, each little bit of achievement slowly increasing the desire to do more.

Her first tentative steps were with a walking frame which slid on wheels; later she progressed to the small wheel-less frame which she was still using at the beginning of 1987. With her new mobility and good diet her weight began to drop and the ulcers on her legs, as daily dressings continued, began to heal nicely. A very difficult nursing decision, though, concerned the ulcers on her feet. With continued immobility they might have dried out more quickly but possibly only at the permanent cost of independence. As it is, walking is painful still and the healing slow. When Miss A finally went home from the Centre just before Christmas 1986, her feet were swathed in dressings which needed to be changed every day.

The Centre, she reflected, really is 'a home from home'. There's no routine. You can make yourself a cup of tea whenever you like. There's no 'lights out'. Of course you put the overhead light off if someone in your room needs to rest, but you can keep your own reading light on all night if you like. And if the senior nurse sees you awake in the early hours she might pop in to ask if you'd like a cup of tea. If you can get about, you can go and join in social events in the day unit or go right outside the Centre.

You ask for your own pills and then, as you get better and more self-sufficient, you keep them by you just as you would at home. Oh — and the food's marvellous, whatever you like and steak and roast meat available even on weekdays. And her GP would stop by about once every two weeks to see how she was getting on.

Having left the ward, Miss A still comes in on Mondays and Wednesdays and Fridays to have her dressings changed and spend some time in the day unit. Every other day a district nurse calls at her home. For Christmas and New Year she went back into the Centre for a few days and had a marvellous time. She reckoned there must have been nearer 70 for Christmas lunch than the projected 50 and on New Year's Eve she stayed up talking till 3 am and on New Year's Day had been able to help out by taking the telephone calls since they were short-handed on the ward because of staff illness. She'd done that before sometimes when she'd been an in-patient, looked after the phone in the early evenings when everyone else was busy. And all this from someone who'd been unable to move and scarcely had the will to try six months earlier.

Back in her own flat, with the home help busy in the kitchen and a friend just called in for tea, Miss A said she couldn't imagine what she would have done without the Centre — just gone into a home, she supposed, since she could never have come home alone from hospital in the state she was in then. 'A lovely place' she and her friend agreed, to be recommended to anyone.

So lovely, you might think, that it would be hard to leave, creating its own kind of dependence, but it doesn't seem to work like that. The homeliness of the Centre, the sense of safety there, seems to make it a secure base for adventuring rather than a retreat. As Miss A said, it's not that hard to leave when you know that there's somewhere you are cared about, somewhere you can go back to as need arises, be it for a ten-minute chat or a re-admission.

Home from home

Miss A's description of her time in the Centre features several of the elements that were deliberately planned into the approach to patients in order to make it more like home than hospital, in order to foster patient autonomy. Drugs, for instance. Miss A had noted as significantly different from hospital the fact that she was responsible for her own pills. This was one of the earliest steps implemented (not without some initial discomfort for nurses accustomed to keeping the drug rounds under their control) towards making the idea of patient autonomy a reality. As a notice for new patients says, 'There are no drug rounds because we are not a hospital. We would like you to take your tablets as you would at home.' At first the nursing staff may keep the drugs but patients decide when to take them. You have only to sit at the nurses' station (a table, a chair and a filing cabinet in the middle of the ward area) for a short time to hear the regular conversation that goes:

> 'I think it's time for my pills.'
> 'If you say so. What do you take?'

As soon as they can, patients look after their own medication. And this has worked perfectly well. Better to take responsibility now, in a place where there's room for discussion or a word of advice. Then you're likely to go home competent and feeling on top of things.

Respect for the patient is fundamental to the Centre's ethos and immensely conducive to self-respect. It shows itself right from admission in other small ways. Although a person's physical condition may be a prime indicator, the mixture of single and four-bedded rooms affords some scope for patients to choose between company and solitude. Similarly, patients are asked what they'd like to be called, surname, Christian name or nickname. Any patient is free to remain Mrs Smith, but mostly it works out as Christian names all round for patients and staff (except from patients to GPs — it would take a lot to undo the tradition of 'Doctor X' there).

These small things matter because they all say you're still Mary Jones, not the chest in the fifth bed. Another of them is the much-praised quality and choice of food coming from the catering service located in the old Lambeth Hospital (again, it's a sign of more than itself — an indication to patients that they are important, are valued). And yet another is the fact that a patient's notes are common property for staff and patient. Patients and relatives are positively encouraged not only to read but to write in the notes themselves if they want to. Although only a few have as yet done so, a lot of the recording is done by quoting patients' own words about how they feel.

The notes are actually kept in the form of SOAP notes, that is to say subjective comment (the patient's own description of how she/he feels), objective comment (what the staff observe), analysis (of causes — if any) and plan (what's to be done about it): as it might be, entirely hypothetically:

> S. I had a terrible night. I do wish I could get a good night's sleep.
> O. Mr Z was awake at least five times during the night, coughing and sometimes panicking about being unable to breathe.
> A. Chest still very congested.
> P. Discuss medication with GP and ask physio to demonstrate best position for Mr Z to lie in order to breathe more easily.

The notes are written in by nurses, GPs, physios, OTs, speech therapist, dietician, maybe a relevant visitor like someone from the St Thomas' Terminal Care Support Team, and they often give a vivid and feeling picture of a patient and of the care offered. I wonder in how many medical establishments' notes you find remarks like 'Do remember sherry is one of the things that Mr Z can still enjoy' or 'S. I feel old and useless. P. Suggest lots of cuddles.'

Miss A also noticed and appreciated the lack of routine, particularly after the general hospital where the care was excellent but 'regimented'. This is clearly germane to the business of getting back to being yourself, doing for yourself. To be able to read as long as you like, make tea when you like gives you a sense of control over your own life. These small but decisive signs of your autonomy may vary from patient to patient. For one it was being able to bring her budgie in with her; for another it was being able to take his usual daily bath at 5 am (a slight case of gritted teeth for staff and the re-acknowledgement that offering patients freedom from routine is harder work than having a set timetable).

And behind all this hard work to promote patient self-determination is also knowledge, beyond that which usually obtains in the busy ward of a general hospital, of the patient's family and home circumstances. For Centre staff the patient is never just an illness nor even just Mrs AZ with painful arthritis, but Mrs AZ who lives alone on the fourth floor in a flat that she likes, which is OK when the lifts are working, who has meals on wheels and home help and a very pleasant neighbour who has unfortunately just had a slight stroke himself . . . and so on. This comprehensiveness of knowledge comes from listening to the patient, from the working together of various professionals, from home visits by Centre staff, from information from community services and from GPs (usefully supplemented on occasion by application to the GP's practice receptionist) not to mention the fact — which everyone does — that this is a friendly place where relatives or neighbours come to visit patients and stay to chat with staff. One GP said of his experience with the Centre that 'friendly, competent, perceptive, above all caring staff encourage you to offer their services to a wide range of people'.

Within the Centre, patients really do look on it as *their* place. Two patients were heard discussing the matter on the ward one day. One averred that the Centre belonged to Dr M, her GP, and the other argued even more vehemently that it was theirs, their own. Certainly a casual visitor is quite likely to be dealt with by a patient, offered guidance or a cup of tea.

So, a sense of responsibility comes along with an awareness of your independence and this is reflected in the way that patients can come to care about one another, not leaving everything to the nurses but being prepared to make their own decisions. When a patient died before her relatives could get there, it was her fellow patients who picked a flower to put on her, said prayers round her and then asked that she stay with them in the room, in her own bed, for a while.

It's in no sense to underestimate the medical care provided at the Centre to say that so often there is, additionally, a perception of other, not strictly medical needs which can have very therapeutic results. Mr B had lung cancer, already quite advanced when it was discovered. After radiotherapy he was admitted to the Centre, depressed and withdrawn, ready to turn his face to the wall and die. It was a nurse who asked if she couldn't get him something to read or some music to listen to who discovered that his time in the Scots Guards had been very important to him, that he would like some military magazines and some bagpipe music and above all he would like to go to see the Changing of the Guard. This was duly arranged, as was a much-desired trip out to the cinema. None of this kept Mr B alive, but it did alter the quality of his last two months. He felt in charge of himself again and took himself home from the Centre to sort out his family affairs before he died.

Working at it

If I'm making all this sound rather simple, that's a mistake because it isn't. It's in the air there now and was written into the hopes for the Centre from the beginning, but the transition from idea to reality wasn't and isn't easy. Patients are, after all, unwell, often very unwell, a state in which the prospect of lying back and being looked after, hospital corners, routines and all, is very seductive. It wasn't as straightforward as it sounds for Miss A to take those first painful steps. And it hasn't been all plain

19

sailing for nurses to jettison parts of traditional training in favour of offering the subtle support necessary to help patients be independent.

It's harder work to respond to people as a whole, including their as-yet-unrealised potential, people who can, of course, be awkward and cantankerous especially when they're ill. Fostering patient autonomy has nothing laissez-faire about it. As another GP has described it, talking about the way that patients and their families are supported at the Centre:

> This is a very elusive quality of the Centre and one that is illustrated in nearly all the patients that have been admitted. It depends on friendliness and approachability of the staff together with a personal interest in the patient and their family and a lack of rules and regulations and restrictions. There is always, however, an educational undercurrent so that patients are not allowed to become dependent but are stimulated to look after themselves more effectively.

Recently Mrs C was nearing the end of the time when she could usefully be in the Centre. She'd been out of sorts with everyone, though in reality out of sorts with herself. 'Yes,' she agreed when the senior nurse suggested this, 'I want to be young again and have my children need me.' In conversation with Mrs C it became apparent that what she wanted more than anything, from among the options that were open to her, was to go home, to be in her own place. To this end she co-operated with all the tasks set her, like regularly washing and dressing herself (this sort of agreed contract is a technique used when it seems likely to help). Then it came to the meeting of Mrs C, her offspring, GP and nurse to discuss her future. And the offspring and GP were sure that they knew what would be best for Mrs C, and it wasn't to go home alone. The nurse felt that her role in this conference was to support and encourage Mrs C to say what she really felt, really wanted. It wasn't enough to be spoken for, she needed to put her own case so that the people concerned for her heard it. This was hard for her. She was used to looking to the more confident younger and professional people who had no inhibitions about proffering their opinions. It took two hours' talking for Mrs C to begin to explain herself and for her family and her doctor to take in how she felt. The result was a change of approach by everyone concerned and a plan to support her in her own home. Before that her positive desires, not fully expressed, had been taken as negative awkwardness.

And when a patient does, as Mrs C did, take hold of his or her own life, then the Centre staff feel that they've done what they're there for. Another nurse recently had to take a patient with a broken leg to casualty at St Thomas' and here the patient refused pointblank to have her heart tested until the doctor explained to her properly why he wanted to do it. He was mildly dumbfounded, but the nurse from the Centre was simply proud of her.

3 Nurse-Advocates

I like the friendliness of the Centre. You're all friendly and
caring. It's like a family. People care about people.

(Voluntary helper)

The subtle support which enables patients to remain in control is
the business of the whole team, but the workers who are perhaps
most crucial to the patient's confidence and self-respect are those
in daily contact with her or him — the nurses. And a lot more is
demanded of nurses at the Centre than just looking after people,
however beautifully, warmly or efficiently.

The nurses are relatively few in number: up until summer 1987
one senior nurse, two sisters, ten RGN, four SEN and five
auxiliaries, with a subsequent re-arrangement involving an
increase in the number of sisters to three.

A certain relaxation
The first challenge for these nurses is to be able to abandon some
traditional emphases: orderliness and routine, neat beds, ward
rounds, a right time for doing things. An essential attribute of
Centre nurses is flexibility, an ability to respond to the need of
the moment: saying 'fine' instead of 'certainly not' if a patient
wants to have a bath at 5 am, not forbidding alcohol but
negotiating one whisky a day, being able to restrain your own
competence in favour of letting a husband or wife attend to the
physical needs of a dying person if that's what the couple wants.

The willingness to involve relatives in nursing care like this
has proved invaluable. Mrs D, for instance, was very upset when
she realised that she wasn't going to be able to die in her own

home and her husband was depressed because he had wanted to look after her until the end but it was getting too much for him to manage. They were visited at home by Centre staff, then they were both admitted to the Centre and Mr D was able to go on caring for his wife with back-up from the nurses. She died peacefully and he, while grieving, was at least relieved of the guilt he would have felt had he 'failed' to look after her to the end.

Knowing when to step back, requires, as well as flexibility, a clear-sighted view of patients, a willingness to get to know them and their families. Being familiar with patients' home circumstances, noticing their likes and dislikes, finding out about their hopes and fears, all are vital to the enterprise of shared health care. Take Mrs E, for example. Elderly, so arthritic that she could barely move around and had to be helped to eat, she used to come into the ward from time to time when her husband wasn't well enough to cope. On one such occasion her husband had been admitted to hospital. And this time her bed sores, usually very responsive to treatment, stubbornly refused to heal. A dawning suspicion on the part of her nurse, followed up with sympathetic questioning, eventually elicited the information that Mrs E had been deliberately not co-operating with the treatment. This was because she was convinced that her husband had gone into hospital with cancer and would die. She was so depressed about this that she wanted to die herself and, having no ready means of killing herself but having heard somewhere that untreated bed sores could lead to septicaemia, had decided to die that way. The treatment in this case was easy — the honest reassurance that her husband did not have cancer and was not going to die.

Or take the case of Mrs F, a patient originally referred for out-patient physiotherapy for pelvic problems. It gradually came out that she was also worried about a problem of continence. She was given advice about this and then, in further conversations with her special nurse, it became apparent that she was very lonely and still mourning the death of a best-beloved child. The 'treatment' then extended from physio appointments and nurse counselling into invitations to join in social events. In the words of one of the sisters,

> She was last seen when volunteering to help at one of the
> Centre's jumble sales. Her pain and incontinence remain a

problem but she regained social contact and talked about her bereavement during stages of emptiness and despair. She was able to pick up her life again which may not have occurred had she been referred to a hospital clinic for physiotherapy.

In both these examples, the patient's fears were noticed by that patient's special nurse. On the ward the special nurse is practically always the patient's key worker and therefore responsible for co-ordinating the patient's treatment as well as for forming a particular bond with that patient. The special nurse will liaise with the GP; see that arrangements are made for any treatment or investigation prescribed, e.g. accompany her patient to X-ray at St Thomas' or consult with a therapist within the Centre; write in the patient's notes; see that in her own absence the responsibility is delegated to another named nurse; write the discharge letter to the GP. Occasionally, if a physio or OT is particularly closely involved with an in-patient then they may share the responsibility with the special nurse. On the day unit (which we'll come to in more detail in chapter seven), the situation has been more complicated, with a therapist more than likely to be the key worker.

In an article in *The Guardian* (3 December 1986), Angela Wilkinson wrote:

> In an ideal world where the NHS could afford to pay all parties equally and they could have equal status, the dispute [between different medical disciplines] could be resolved by placing the responsibility for integration of care into the hands of the main contributor to care.

Which makes the Lambeth Community Care Centre something of a foretaste of an ideal world because that's exactly what they do there, having worked out the system for themselves (it all depends, of course, on the goodwill of poorly paid staff who don't get anything extra for the responsibility even if they do get more job satisfaction).

Although it seems like second nature now, the system whereby every trained nurse is responsible for individual patients had to be learnt. It caused some anxieties in early days just as giving patients responsibility for their own drugs didn't come all that easily at first.

When the ward opened it operated for a while in the traditional way with information being passed down from sister to staff nurse to enrolled nurse to auxiliary. But this soon proved cumbersome in a small unit and ill-suited to multi-disciplinary, patient-centred working. As the other sister tells it:

> We found in both areas, but particularly on the ward, that this system was inefficient and impractical, mainly because our patients are often complex admissions involving relatives, GPs, community health services and members of the multi-disciplinary team . . . and it was unreasonable to expect one person to retain all this information and constantly hand it over to the other members of staff. Also, and as importantly, we were unable to give individualised care; this was lost in central organisation. After much discussion by nurses and members of the multi-disciplinary team, it was decided that a key worker set-up be implemented. Each trained member of staff is responsible for a patient's total care . . . This resulted in extra responsibility and decision-making permeating down through the team.

Around the same time as this way of working was becoming established, the nurses also decided communally that the status-linked St Thomas' uniforms which they'd been wearing were a mistake and in the spring of 1986 they started wearing identical simple blue dresses.

Along with the informality, flexibility and sense of personal responsibility goes a generally greater exposure to patients than usual. If you are to spend a lot of time talking with as well as doing things for people, if you are to get to know people's feelings and attitudes, if you are going to be personal with them, then, given the Centre's abjuration of patronage, you have to be available to the patient in a relationship of some kind of mutuality. It would be a romantic falsification to suggest that the relationship is wholly equal; there is bound to be some imbalance between cared for and carer. But more than in most medical establishments, the nurses accept that if they can ask people personal questions then they can be questioned in turn, if they can be familiar with patients then patients can be familiar with them, that they can expect to be greeted with 'You're in a bad mood today. What's wrong?' from a patient who expects a proper answer.

This abandonment of some kinds of self-protection makes demands of the whole personality which not all nurses can or want to meet. A few have found the Centre not to their taste and left. One decided that she wasn't cut out for nursing at all and went off, happily, to be a gardener instead. But most expand into the extra responsibility and freedom. And, as a certain attitude towards the job becomes more and more intrinsic to the Centre, so new nurses seem to pick it up more and more quickly. It was a comparatively recently arrived nurse who on her own initiative served a woman with lunch as she sat with the body of her recently dead son. A year or so earlier, the senior nurse said, no nurse would have dreamt that anyone might want such a thing; they would have ushered relatives swiftly away from a death bed for a cup of tea in sister's room (not that there is any such thing as a square, shut-doored sister's room here; instead there's a kind of light, glass, triangular area which is used by all and sundry).

Asserting themselves

Patient autonomy can best be recognised, valued and supported by nurses who are comfortable with their own autonomy. And yet the hardest thing of all for the nurses, however open, flexible and caring, has been to learn an assertive decisiveness, a willingness to take complete responsibility. Even now, the senior nurse acknowledged ruefully, younger nurses respond beautifully to being ordered around, will jump to it with alacrity and without resentment if, in frustration, she should shout about something which she can see needs doing. She'd be only too delighted if someone would sometimes argue back and even more pleased if they would take the risk of doing things off their own bat. It isn't just that she very occasionally feels that all the most painful decisions still gravitate in her direction, but more that she'd like to see nurses shaken out of that nice responsiveness.

In December 1985, at one of the Centre's regular audit meetings to monitor and evaluate its own progress, the subject for discussion was chosen by lucky dip from notes made by everyone present about where they thought communication needed to be improved. The topic pulled out of the hat was 'Still some reluctance in nurses to suggest or initiate — not noticeable in senior nurses.' The meeting proceeded to discuss the problem for an hour, ranging over concomitant issues as various as greater accuracy and clarity needed in note-keeping and how junior nurses could be given the confidence to ask more questions of senior nurses and GPs. A year later, a team meeting of Centre staff was addressing the question of nurses' willingness to take responsibility in a crisis. The trigger for the discussion was an incident when a patient had fallen in the Centre. The nurse had rung the GP but been unable to press her view that he should come to visit in face of his reluctance. It was reported to the team that the GPs who'd heard about this at the previous audit meeting had agreed that there were occasions when the nurse must make the decision and *tell* the doctor and that they would in future co-operate by responding to such messages, leaving any discussion until afterwards — just as all decisions within the Centre by whomsoever are open to discussion afterwards.

Learning to 'tell' a doctor rather than responding to a doctor is quite a few steps on from simply learning to ask questions of the GP, a measure of progress during the first year. Nurses' self-confidence is so crucial to patients' self-confidence — as well as being necessary on those occasions where quick decisions are called for and no 'senior' on the spot — that serious consideration was being given to making assertiveness training available to the nurses.

Talking it out

The team meeting at which I heard this discussion is itself one of the ways in which nurses coped with their changing role over the first 18 months. At the stage when the system of special nurses had been instituted and everyone was aware of what they were, in theory, trying to do, there was a hiatus, a period when there was a slightly alarmed, rather hesitant feeling around. The nurses knew that they were moving on to new territory in trying to put into practice ideas about patient autonomy while, of course, wanting to maintain a good standard of care, and they weren't sure whether they were getting it right.

'Difficulties were experienced and practice was often found to revert to routines. Patients were not always involved in their own care.' At this point an outside catalyst proved very valuable. The senior nurse (research) in the West Lambeth Health Authority, as well as offering necessary personal support to the senior nurse at the Centre, was invited to help generally and introduced 'quality circle' meetings of all concerned in nursing care, a forum for them to examine their own practice.

Under his guidance, in the words of one sister:

> We listed the differences in our care provision from a hospital and agreed to set a philosophy and standards of care . . . The team started to meet regularly for one hour a fortnight. A brainstorming session was held with everyone identifying problems. Our facilitator led the group to select which problem to solve first. Problems tackled by the circle include medication, crime prevention and security, staff hand-overs, system of note-keeping, patient activities, role of the auxiliary, lost washing and individual care. The members tried to resolve issues and problems through action and achieving goals set. The meetings have resulted in the staff feeling more involved with the over-all running of the Centre. The skills of the facilitator have been important in producing change . . . The membership of the circle has now expanded to involve all the Centre staff including therapists and administrative staff.

They are called team meetings now but they still operate on the same basis of brainstorming and then putting the problems raised into an agreed order of priority. And they're still covering the waterfront from missing notes and the time it takes to get discharge letters written to the whole relationship between ward and day unit.

One thing done in the early days was to re-articulate exactly what they thought the Centre and in particular the nursing there was all about.

> Goal: to provide an alternative health-care service bridging the gap between hospital and home through continuity of care within the community, the aim of the care being to

maintain an individual within the community by encouraging participation in care and returning control to the individual patient.

Standard I: each patient is treated as an individual patient.

Standard II: each patient has a right to choose and make decisions about their own care and treatment.

Standard III: the patients receive appropriate care aimed at maximising their independence and maintaining them in the community.

Standard IV: care for the patient includes the involvement and support of other 'carers' in the community and the education of the community as a whole.

Standard V: care is provided in a friendly and homely place.

Standard VI: communication is an essential part of individualised care.

As well as making general demands on the whole personality, these standards, attitudes, call them what you will, also involve an expansion of skills beyond those directly related to nursing sick people in bed. Before any planned admission, for instance, a nurse from the Centre, probably with a therapist, will visit the patient at home or in the general hospital. They will be required to contribute their opinion about the appropriateness of admission and the purpose of admission. This seems to work most often in the direction of the nurse OKing an admission about which the GP has been doubtful rather than the other way round.

In fact, in the very early days the nurses, while feeling their own way, also thought that the GPs weren't trusting them to cope with anything not absolutely straightforward. Looking back now, the project GPs say that they didn't at first admit all the patients they might have done because they were so concerned for the Centre to avoid mistakes that they were overly cautious, not mistrusting the nursing but mistrusting their own decision making, stepping cautiously. But that is now a thing of the past.

And some of the progress is due to deliberate efforts made by the nurses to help GPs to catch up with what they felt they could offer. At the audit meeting in July 1986, for example, the role of the nurses in the day unit was discussed and the minutes record:

The nurses had identified an area in which they had done a lot of work which had not previously been acknowledged or recorded by them. This was mainly in the role of nurse counsellor. Many patients who came to the Centre for whatever reason would often seek the nurses out for guidance over personal matters. These sessions were now being written up and appointments given for subsequent visits. GPs would always receive a discharge letter after a visit. It was emphasised that there were many areas where referrals could be made specifically for this type of care.

The patient's advocate

The boundaries of what constitutes nursing care are being gently pushed back all the time at the Centre. In the day unit in particular strictly traditional nursing blurs around the edges into other kinds of care. If the health of the whole person is at issue, there's no point in making a distinction between counselling about continence and talking about grief, between advice about breast-feeding and hearing about a young mother's loneliness, between changing a dressing and encouraging someone to see the dentist.

It's all part of reinforcing patients' independence. Whether it involves planning together a programme of hygiene and self-care or offering warm friendly support for learning to go out to the shops again, it could be called social skills training, too. The labels don't matter much except in so far as they help the nurses and their colleagues to recognise what is happening in terms of the extension of their abilities and to plan for further training and improvement.

Another development which was showing signs of burgeoning after the Centre had been in action for about 18 months is in work within groups. Those nurses who are interested are beginning to get the opportunity to take part — with therapists and the Centre's community link worker — in the setting up of mutual support groups for patients.

In whatever direction the content of the nursing role changes, though, it is all an outworking of the essential attitude to patients which informs the Centre's work. The senior nurse describes all the work done for and with the patient as springing from a sense of yourself as the patient's advocate. This is a very different view from that pertaining in a more hierarchical world, where patients can feel that all staff are 'them' over and against 'us' patients. The concept of advocacy for the patient embraces all the personal concern for the patient, the listening and attentiveness but adds a commitment to be on the patient's side, to help the patient do what seems best to her or him. The first practical example which springs to mind is that of a woman with cancer secondaries who was quite clear in her own mind that she did not want further treatment of a particular kind but who could not bring herself to say this to her doctor. The role of the Lambeth Community Care Centre nurse in this situation is to be on her side, to support her in her own decision, to encourage her to express it for herself but also, if really necessary, to speak on her behalf.

4 Sharing

From inception to date many problems have been faced and a variety of solutions found. All those involved, project team to current staff, architects to nursing auxiliaries, have learnt from this co-operative, multi-disciplinary approach.

(A GP)

This chapter, more than most, is likely to traipse all over the territory of other chapters, for the co-operative nature of the Centre's work is relevant to all its activities.

For the patient's sake

The rationale for a democratic multi-disciplinary team is to be found in what such teams working well and honestly can achieve for and with patients. It would be hard to find a patient's story which didn't encompasss the contribution of a variety of workers. A multi-faceted concern for a patient's life tends to entail a whole lot of team-work.

The Centre's first orthopaedic admission was of an elderly man who had been in St Thomas' Hospital with a broken hip. He no longer needed the teaching hospital's medical resources but was in no state to go home either. When he'd been at home his meals had been supplied by his daughter-in-law, but his son had unexpectedly just died so both daughter-in-law and Mr G were shocked and grieving. Mr G was also confused and incontinent. The GP thought of the Centre, but wasn't sure if they could cope with all of Mr G's problems within a relatively short stay (this was in the days before they had the confidence to know when to break the guideline of 28 days' maximum stay for the sake of a planned rehabilitation). A nurse and OT visited Mr G on the ward and decided that it would be possible; they also, as always thinking ahead and wanting to be clear about future prospects, checked with Mr G's daughter-in-law that she was willing to take on some responsibility for him again in due course.

It was reported from the hospital to the Centre that Mr G had misunderstood and developed a great fear that the Centre was an old people's home where he was to be 'put away'. So the OT visited him for a second time specifically to reassure him about this before he was admitted to the Centre.

Within the Centre there was a definite plan for Mr G's rehabilitation, with nurses and therapists working together to help him to become lucid, continent and mobile again. At first he wanted to sleep all the time, but he began to co-operate in the treatment when he understood what the alternatives were if he didn't become fit enough to go home. Having his own GP to look after him was a positive bonus. Indeed, a distinct marker of his progress out of confusion was when he first saw his doctor and said, 'Coo, doc, what are you doing here?' Gradually he began to walk again with a frame.

When it looked like nearly time for him to be discharged, the OT and a district nurse visited his home with his relatives in order to see how physically possible it was all going to be. The agreement reached was that he would be supported at home with home help, meals on wheels, district nurses' visits, etc. Also, Mr G, initially hostile to the idea, changed his mind about the day unit, decided he would like to come back for two days a week and then became very attached to this routine. Mr G was said, though 'jolly with us', to be not altogether easy at home, but his daughter-in-law was better able to cope because she could drop into the Centre from time to time for 'coffee and a moan'.

The staff were particularly pleased about this admission, partly because it was the first orthopaedic one but more because, had there not been some care 'intermediate between the hospital and the home' available, then it's likely that Mr G would have ended up in long-term care, dependent on an institution for the rest of his life.

It is especially rewarding to see someone blossom from withdrawal or confusion or despair into a lively interest in being alive. Mr H was 70 years old and 'rotund' (Centre staff always pick their words carefully, respectfully; neither in conversation nor on paper did I ever come across a superior or dismissive description of a patient). He was referred to the Centre with oedema and difficulty in breathing. He had had previous admissions to hospitals with congestive cardiac failure and had long been quite a heavy drinker. At first he seemed very willing and friendly but, as he got used to being in the Centre, sank into what seemed a more basic state of mind — low spirits and a self dislike which accounted for his self-neglect.

No longer outgoing and co-operative, he grew more and more tearful and eventually, bemoaning his own valuelessness, suicidal, demanding a knife to end it all with. His GP suggested blood samples and these indicated the possibility of hepatitis. Another dilemma: a very practical basic guideline is 'no infectious diseases'. But Mr H was already there, had let Centre staff know his feelings and would probably have experienced a move as a great rejection. So he stayed. His GP kept in close touch and also in consultation with St Thomas' and simple barrier nursing was introduced.

Meanwhile, earlier in Mr H's admission he had automatically been screened by the Centre's dentist who looks at the teeth of all patients over 60 for both research and therapeutic reasons. Examination and questioning revealed the fact that Mr H hadn't been able to eat properly for a year. His dentures fitted so badly that he wore them only in company, never for eating on his own. He'd been afraid to do anything about it because he thought that it would be costly as well as because of the inertia of depression.

Mr H was beginning to get better physically when his new dentures arrived (after four visits to the dentist). 'This, combined with a great loss in weight . . . and gradually feeling better, seemed to be the turning point.' He became open to discussing the future and at a meeting with friends, relatives, staff and someone from social services, a scheme for his support at home was evolved. 'Interestingly, the highlight of the patient's stay with us was receiving a new set of teeth. This did more than anything to restore his self-image.' Or, as the dentist himself described it, 'He was now able to, as he told me later, "smile and chat up the nurses". Mr H's behaviour was transformed, he became jovial and co-operative . . . It also gave him encouragement in his approach to other problems.'

When the resources of a multi-disciplinary team are truly available, you never quite know who's going to turn out to be crucial for any one patient. Indeed, the balance of what a patient needs from the team may change over time. Mrs I, in her early forties, was referred to the day unit having been found to have multiple sclerosis. At first the physiotherapist was much involved with helping Mrs I to keep her balance but, as new difficulties arose, other workers joined in and Mrs I's progress has subsequently been reviewed monthly by the physio and OT together. The OT and the dietician were both concerned to assist Mrs I with cooking — vital both to have a proper diet for the sake of her health and to be able to do the cooking herself for the sake of her morale and sense of control. The Centre OT liaised with the community OTs about the provision of aids for Mrs I at home, a stairlift, for instance, when climbing the stairs became too hard.

However, with any deteriorating or potentially deteriorating illness the increasing physical limitations are accompanied by the considerable emotional problems of coming to terms with what's happening to you. And that's where Mrs I came into her own as a member of her own health team. She was naturally very depressed by the diagnosis at first and staff felt that they couldn't provide enough psychological support. It became apparent, however, that there were a number of people in the neighbourhood with MS or similar neurological diseases, so the OTs started a group where patients could discuss their problems together. Mrs I became slowly more confident, more willing to tell people — strangers even — that she had MS and, when the planned sessions of what came to be known as the Backing Group reached an end, she was a major force in getting it to carry on under its own steam and without any need for staff help.

Working together

These examples (the latter, incidentally, showing a supportive medical team in action without either nurse or doctor playing a leading role) reinforce the point made earlier that the Centre's inclusive way of working inevitably reaches out beyond the front door of the place itself. Every non-emergency admission to ward or day unit is preceded by a visit of assessment by Centre staff. Before discharge, too, a therapist will often visit a patient's home to work out what physical problems there will be and how the patient can best be helped to manage. And there is a lot of to-ing and fro-ing with the community-based medical and social services.

At the (entirely random) weekly meeting of day unit staff that I went to (one and a half hours of concentration before patients arrive), 12 patients were discussed. As well as a review of physical and emotional progress or adaptation — with hip replacement, ulcers, malnutrition, bronchitis, strokes, osteo-arthritis, rheumatoid arthritis, back pain, incontinence and depression — there was also, in every case, concern for the patient's social and physical environment and how that affected their potential recovery and well-being. District nurses, home helps and relatives were among those whose views were quoted (as well, of course, as the patients' own views) or whose support was referred to. Five home visits by Centre staff were mentioned — by varying combinations of nurse, OT, physio, speech therapist and social worker.

More than once the social worker (a relatively newly filled position, with the social worker employed by the local social services area office but located at the Centre) had ended up talking housing with people: sorting out housing benefit; advising people who wanted to move nearer to children or out of unsuitably high or damp flats or even out of solitude into a home. And in all these situations the housing matter was also a health matter, whether because the steps were an agony for swollen joints or because the isolation brought on panic attacks.

In most cases the GP was already deeply involved, but in a couple of instances the meeting decided that there was some scope for mediation. One family just needed to be properly introduced to their newish GP whom they felt they didn't know well enough to ask questions; another situation needed some explanation on paper for the GP group-practice file so that members of the same practice didn't go on re-admitting the patient to the Centre without reference to a pattern that had become visible after several admissions by different doctors.

Doubts and hesitations

This may all sound obvious, easy and everyday, which in a sense it is, but the quality of communication within the Centre, its palpably open and democratic atmosphere was not simply picked out and put on like a new dress. It is the outcome of a much more costly and sweaty process of change from within. What they started with was a small group of people with a more or less common vision of what the Centre might be like but also with all their doubts, anxieties, insecurities and defence mechanisms.

It all began with a burst of enthusiasm, but, after about six months of operation, there was a realisation that all was not necessarily well just because beds were filled, the therapy departments in full swing and the supportive underpinning of inter-connected management and consultative meetings in place.

The structure is basically sound and works well. The Centre Management Team (administrator, senior nurse, GP — rotating, therapist — rotating, and now chairperson of the Centre Advisory Group, who must be a local lay person) meets fortnightly to take executive decisions about the Centre's work. And members of the CMT serve, between them, on just about every other kind of group, formal or informal, going — team meetings, ward meetings, day unit meetings, garden committee, arts committee, education committee, research advisory group, etc — and so are thoroughly informed about attitudes, opinions and feelings within the Centre.

Then there's the monthly audit meeting open to all Centre staff and all GPs for the regular evaluation of the Centre's work. Sometimes they concentrate on individual patients: was the admission appropriate? Was the patient given the right kind of help? How did the liaison with other agencies work? Could a similar situation be better handled in any way in future? Had Centre staff learnt anything about their own strengths which would make them more willing to take further risks another time? And sometimes they take a whole area of work: the rehabilitation of stroke patients or communications within the Centre or relationships with other bits of the health service.

This structure is certainly no hindrance to sharing but in the winter of 1985/6 it wasn't proving enough. It was, after all the initial excitement, a low period, a time of uphill struggle. One or two of the project GPs, who had been working for this for years, were putting a lot of time into meetings and informal visits and a lot of energy into anxiously monitoring their own use of the

Centre for patients, and they felt suddenly anticlimactic, more drained than energised.

We've already looked at the nurses' hesitations which led to the setting up of quality circles. The OTs, glad of the opportunity to use the full range of their skills, felt that other staff, and GPs in particular, did not recognise or make use of that range of skills. The community link worker, just taking up her job then, was quite sure that her colleagues did not have much idea what she was *for*.

Sharing includes having enough trust in one another to admit to weaknesses and this was, in the early days, one of the hardest things of all for the team. It was badly needed, for instance in the relationship between GPs, stepping cautiously in their use of the Centre, and nurses, just beginning to realise that they had a different role in prospect here. The putting up of drips is an activity well within the GP's repertoire and an everyday matter in the Centre now. But at the beginning GPs who hadn't done it for a while and nurses still used to saying 'yes, sir' had a few fraught moments of buck passing. 'What do you need?' 'Well, er, just bring me the usual, you know.' But as soon as they were able to admit to doubts, like not being sure exactly what equipment you did need at a particular moment, then it was easy to work out together what to do. But it meant nurses claiming knowledge for themselves, doctors admitting to less than absolute confidence and knowledgeability and both of them coming out from behind professional barricades.

This kind of 'coming out' feels vulnerable. The uncertain feeling around had quite a bit to do with guardedness and lack of communication between the different disciplines. As the administrator put it, looking back from a year later, it was hard for people to stop acting in an automatically defensive manner. Most came from bigger hospitals where departments can work in isolation from each other and under considerable pressure. Often, or so I heard tell, people's experience had been that there could be competitiveness or even, sadly, enmity between departments. Staff were at this stage scratchy, doubtful about their own ability to do what was required but all tending to keep this to themselves, thinking it a private problem, not shared.

The smallness of the Centre, however, means that when there is a problem it can't be hidden or ignored for long. So there was a general acknowledgement of uneasiness, a recognition that for some reason or other they had a choice in front of them between doing what they had set out to do or sliding back into something more familiar. At one point, when feelings of discomfort were prevalent, some staff did begin to hanker a bit for the smack of firm government and, says the senior nurse, a real crunch point arrived: did they go autocratic 'just like everyone else' or did they make a desperate try for real democracy?

They chose the latter — they were after all there because they believed in the Centre as originally conceived — but it was experienced at the time as really rather a desperate bid. Strains were showing. People felt misunderstood. There were tears at meetings. But then there wasn't any time for mopping up, working out why. Meetings had to be disciplined. Patients were waiting.

The senior staff decided that what they badly needed was more time together without the pressure of agendas. So they started to meet once a week outside the Centre for informal, off-the-record conversation about work. When, after a bit, it seemed they were getting so far but no further, they invited the project GPs to join them once a month, in part to act as catalysts — to help, as someone new coming into a group often can, the existing members to sort out their difficulties. Even so, these weekly meetings often ended still with a sense that only a tiny bit of a tangled skein had been unravelled. So, they decided they needed yet more leisured time together and a senior staff weekend away was organised.

This was February and the weekend was to be in May. The intervening period the administrator describes as the Centre's doldrums. It wasn't that there was now any thought of reneging on the Centre's commitment to democratic intermediate health care. It was more as if everyone were waiting for the weekend and meantime just going on day after day.

The senior nurse describes a sensation not of unhappiness, not of lack of conviction but of isolation. She felt she was having to push other people while having nowhere to put her own worries. Before the weekend she was almost ready to throw in the towel out of a sort of weariness. Three weeks beforehand she found the place suddenly deserted. Everyone had gone off to a meeting without telling her where it was to be. While searching for her missing colleagues, she noticed a smell of gas but she was so fraught that, when she found them, she spent some minutes berating them for their lack of consideration before thinking to mention the possible gas leak — and emptying the room in seconds.

After the weekend

As the weekend got nearer, she wasn't the only one to start regarding the occasion with dread rather than with expectation. Now she says that, if she were ever involved in starting another new venture, she would programme just such a weekend into it about six months after the launch. It was a considerable turning point. People tend to talk in terms of Before the Weekend and After the Weekend. But it can only have been so effective because, for all their uncertainties, staff were committed to the idea of the Centre and, for all their insecurities, prepared to share their feelings as well as their thoughts.

There was a lot of talking and a lot of emotion expressed. With more time at their disposal, staff were able to say what they felt about one another, among other things, and one result was that problems which had been seen as entirely individual were recognised as communal, sensations of isolation were relieved. However, the detail of what went on remains unclear. And rightly. It was essentially a private occasion.

One result, though, is that since then there has been a freedom to speak truth within the staff team. Of course, it's not complete or perfect, but people are observably frank about their own reactions, ready to say 'I'm not sure if I should have done that', and prepared to comment equally unreservedly on one another's work. And they are heard because such comment is not experienced as an assault on the recipient's professional dignity but merely as a reflection by a fellow team member sharing a concern for the patient and a common desire to learn all the time how to improve the service.

There are still problems. It would be wrong to suggest otherwise. There are members of staff who still think, and say so, that their colleagues don't fully appreciate what it is that they do. At the beginning of 1987 the regular team meetings were turning their attention to snags in communication between the ward and day unit. But it's in the nature of somewhere alive, growing, to go on uncovering difficulties, however tiring that may feel at times. The difference After the Weekend is that, however stubborn problems may appear, however closely they may involve people's feelings, there's an essential orientation towards seeing them as 'ours', towards working on them together.

The senior staff were planning to have a couple of days away together a year on in order to look back at what had happened and forwards at what still needed doing. Meantime, the main impression I took away from my conversations is that they are more concerned that the Centre should fulfil its own ideals, that patients and the locality should be getting a good service, that other people in other places should think of doing likewise, than they are to protect themselves or project a particular professional image. I was told very readily of struggles and setbacks, disappointments and personal failures, particularly in this matter of learning to share, because what staff wanted was a truthful rather than an idealised record of the Centre's beginnings.

5 Good Practice

In brief the Centre does good, looks good and working
there feels good. With the passage of time many of us have
become more confident and the problems we are willing to
address are ever-widening in scope.

(A GP)

What the Centre has meant in the practice of the 40 or so
disparate doctors involved seems to be a loosening up, a bringing
into play of more bits of a professional self, of faculties and skills
which had been lying fallow during the busy round of daily work.
It is as if the Centre has been a space within which to expand.

In the inner city
Working as a GP in the inner city is different from doing the
same job in a small country town. As one GP put it, what is
normal in general practice elsewhere becomes really rather good
practice in the city because of all the additional pressures. Just to
go on producing the care for people which is the hallmark of
good doctoring can be a struggle when you're faced with a
sapping amount of psycho-social need among your patients: poor
housing, poverty and fear exacerbating physical ailments and
manifesting themselves in the depression and anxiety which
bring so many people to the GP's surgery.

Rehousing schemes have often destroyed close neighbour-
hoods and weakened community initiative. Younger people
with get up and go have done just that. Neighbours may be
strangers and visitors are by definition up to no good.

High-rise schemes . . . have left the elderly isolated in the upper floors while the ground is the territory of the car and the street criminal. Telephones are expensive and few will answer to a knock after dark. Thus domiciliary care schemes are hard to maintain. In our cities many have worked hard individually or in groups to reverse these trends, and to provide care and cover under increasing difficulties. Nevertheless brave communities with fewer resources than ever are being asked to take on more illness and handicap. The trickle of need for intermediate care has become a flood.

That's how one of the Centre's GPs sees the area and its needs. It was the same GP who remarked that they'd tried having videos in their waiting room but these never survived more than a couple of days because they were vandalised or stolen. He also pointed out that doing night duty was no fun for anyone and particularly not for a woman — going alone into the heart of one of the huge, slablike estates in the dark carrying a bag which might be supposed to have drugs in it. It felt, like quite a lot of GP work under pressure, lonely.

The existence of such places as the Centre can only help to make work in the city less solitary, more satisfying and therefore more attractive to general practitioners. This Centre has been experienced as offering space for breathing, thinking and meeting colleagues. One of the dangers of dutifully responding to the demands of an inner-city neighbourhood is that a doctor may become very isolated, lacking the opportunity for mutual moral support and the exchange of ideas with people engaged in similar work. 'There is no post-graduate centre in the vicinity and many of the GPs are working in isolation, not knowing who their nearest neighbour is,' wrote another GP. 'The daily coming and going in the Centre, the regular monthly meetings and the excellent facilities in the canteen have resulted in much more interchange and understanding between GPs and their consultant colleagues.'

At the audit and other meetings, in frequent informal contacts, there is room, otherwise lacking, for thought and discussion. Several of the GPs involved are also trainers and the trainees are able to meet regularly in the little seminar room at

43

the Centre, as well as sharing in general discussions and taking in the Centre's attitudes to the practice of medicine. Nor is the increased amount of interaction· restricted to GPs and GP trainees; there is a perhaps even more important extension of the work into reflective, sometimes argumentative partnership with all the members of the primary health-care team. At an audit meeting, when the subject for discussion was the evaluation of the Centre's work to date, one GP present pointed out that the nature of this very meeting, having this discussion was one of the new fruits of the Centre's existence. Where else, he asked, would you get the chance regularly to spend time discussing health issues with GPs, nurses, physios, OTs, dentist, social worker, etc, all meeting on equal terms and with a common commitment?

As the administrator said on another occasion, at the most essential level, in relation to patient care, there was no way that bucks could be passed in either direction. In hospital, she said, it's possible for problems to be dealt with in isolation from the patient's future circumstances. Here, at the Centre, though, everyone shared the same long-term perspective; you and the GP were in it together, you both knew all about the patient's home and there was no question of discharging someone into GP care and then forgetting about them. Equally, there was no temptation for the GP to 'dump' the Centre with a problem since it remained his or her very own problem even if the patient were admitted.

This continuity of care, before, during and after admission, was mentioned by more than one GP as being significant to them and in their view to patients, too. 'The success of the LCCC,' ran one such comment, 'based on patients' feelings, is very much related to the fact that their own family doctor is caring for them and will continue to do so on their return home. Continuity of care is very important in the running of the Centre and could only continue if it remains GP based.'

Another GP, from a different practice, who has been working for and with the Centre since the days of the project team, summed up several of its benefits to local GPs:

Working in south-east London since 1971, one cannot fail to notice the reduction in the service we are given by the local hospitals. At the same time the range of services expected of GPs and the level of their training and expertise has been dramatically improving. A clear 'gap' in care seems to have developed between home-based GPs and community nursing care as opposed to the very high-tech specialist care offered in our DGHs. I perceive the CCC as an attempt to bridge the gap by allowing GPs with the skill and interest to care for their patients in a situation where they have appropriate facilities and staff to comple-ment their clinical skills. From the patient's point of view their care can be flexible and more appropriate to their future needs in the community because of the long-term viewpoint that all GPs have.

This picks out several of the bonuses already mentioned — continuity of care, a long-term view based on three-dimensional personal knowledge and working with other professionals to provide the most suitable kind of care and treatment.

Tools of the trade
In terms of treatment, the Centre offers GPs more than one additional arrow for their quivers. It isn't only an in-patient facility, it's also a day unit where quick and simple out-patient appointments are available with physio, OT, chiropodist, dietician, speech therapist and dentist. Time and again GPs spoke of the value of direct access to such services and of the speed with which their patients could be seen. We shall come back to this in more detail when looking specifically at the day unit but from the GP's point-of-view, the possibility of supplementing his or her own diagnosis and treatment with instant therapy has obviously filled a much-felt need so many are the stories of bad backs and painful injuries swiftly eased. There usually follows some comment on what a pleasant contrast it is to see your patient relieved of pain and re-activated within days rather than having a frustrating weeks' long wait for an out-patient appointment at hospital. The same GP just quoted also summed up what a lot of others had remarked about this amenity:

> I have referred a very large number of people with joint and musculoskeletal symptoms, such as low back strain, sciatica

and cervical spondylosis. At St Thomas' Hospital these need to be seen in the Rheumatology out-patients where there is a very long waiting list. At Guy's direct access to physio is possible but there is still a waiting list and the services are very stretched. The CCC allows GPs, who increasingly have appropriate training and skills, to work with physiotherapists and occupational therapists efficiently, arrange simple aids (such as collars) to be made for their patients and allow rapid remobilisation and return to work without increasing the burden on the very stretched hospital services.

Perhaps 'work with' is one of the crucial phrases there. Even when direct referral to a hospital therapist exists, there isn't the same flexibility as at the Centre where a patient can be seen within the week or even within the day. If a GP thinks such a quick appointment is advisable a phone conversation is enough to arrange it — the paperwork can follow later. The Centre's smallness makes this possible, together with its staff's determination to be a real team. 'The therapists,' writes another GP, 'have always been easy to reach in order to discuss referrals over the phone, and there is no doubt that patients have valued the direct access from surgery.'

There may be yet more potential in the day unit for GPs to discover. Not all of them at present make the same ready use of the all-day stay facility as they do of the popular out-patient therapy services. But then GP use of the Centre is expanding all the time. To recap briefly, it does *not* offer X-ray or casualty since both are already available locally. It *is* equipped for minor surgery (the wart-removing kind) but seldom used for that since most GP surgeries are similarly equipped and teaching hospitals are in any case quite glad to carry out minor procedures as an educational exercise. One or two GPs without their own surgical facilities, though, have been glad of the Centre's. ECG testing is also available there and has been of increasing use over recent months.

As for the medicine practised on the ward, aspects of it have been mentioned already and others will come up later — the rehabilitative work, care for the dying, keeping an eye open while someone is nursed through an acute episode of some kind.

Forty per cent of the patients during the first year, however, were admitted primarily for medical treatment and the range of treatments used has increased over the months, at first tentatively and then with mounting confidence.

The early tentativeness was in part that walking-on-eggshells in order to do nothing to spoil the fleshing-out of the precious concept of the Centre and partly a diffidence about abilities which hadn't been displayed for a while. The setting up of intravenous infusions (drips) and the putting in of catheters are good examples. Both are now done as a matter of course, just as blood samples are now regularly taken by nurses. A skill once learnt soon comes back even if you do have a few sweaty moments when picking up your first catheter in some years. Sometimes it was trainees, fresh from hospital, who showed the way by simply carrying on without thinking about it. And, of course, all doctors do have the relevant training. Some hospital doctors may have practically no experience of general practice, but all GPs were initially trained in hospital (indeed, one GP commented wrily, it's all too easy to find the 'ward roundy' approach still lurking within yourself ready to take over if you're not careful).

One GP suggested that the Centre was not a suitable place for an admission when it looked as if a patient might need some kind of intravenous transfusion. But he was not so much commenting on the average GP's ability to set up a drip as pointing out that great care had to be taken in the choice of venue for an acute emergency admission, especially if it looked as if there were any chance that the stroke or whatever might lead to the patient's death. 'If we admit moribund patients to the CCC and they die shortly after admission, it will not be long before we have a reputation as an institution associated with death.' It's probably a wise caveat, but I see no evidence that anything like that has been happening. In so far as the Centre does have a reputation for being associated with death, it's with the planned care of patients already known to be dying.

GPs are careful about their admissions and that care is not wholly unrelated to the fact that they themselves must visit to settle any patient whom they refer as an emergency and continue to take full medical responsibility. But they have also been gradually exploring the whole range of medicine available to them. There are individual variations in the degree to which they use the Centre and the manner in which they use it. Some have got in the way of regularly utilising the Centre for the care of their terminally ill patients. Often a dying person can't stay at home but doesn't need the busy ward or specialist medicine of the DGH — in fact, it's the last thing they need. Centre staff and some of its GPs have developed, with help from the St Thomas' Terminal Care Support Team, quite an expertise in relieving the distress that may be associated with the final stages of an illness. Using aids like morphine drivers, they have become versed in pain control and have been with their own patients at the end in a way which is perhaps not so common in general practice in the city these days.

Other GPs may hardly ever use the Centre for a dying patient but be particularly attached to its rehabilitative resources or its value as a place for respite care. It is bound to be to some extent a matter of temperament and existing biases (with the everpresent possibility of each GP gradually moving into the less immediately attractive bits of territory). However, they all speak of the Centre as permitting an extension of their practice in some way or other beyond what they were doing before and so as an increase of the means by which they can assist their patients. 'The CCC allows us as GPs to practise primary health care in an "ideal" setting which compensates for the social disadvantages of our patients.'

Miss J, 78 years old, was suffering from diabetes, cellulitis and osteomyelitis of her left foot when admitted to the Centre. She is also almost blind and completely deaf — a condition which made continuity of care by her own doctor within a small, homely unit especially valuable. Her GP kept in close touch with St Thomas's surgical team while treating Miss J with intravenous antibiotics, taking measures to control the diabetes and having her foot dressed regularly. Miss J became well enough to go home again but was able to attend the day unit for continued attention. The same GP also spoke of Mr K who suffered, severely, from Parkinson's Disease. By admitting Mr K to the Centre, where he could be monitored at timed intervals in relation to his tablet-taking, she was able to make a total change in his medication with a resultant improvement in his ability to walk, talk and swallow. She couldn't have taken this risk with the patient at home, lacking 24-hour skilled supervision. The only alternative might have been to 'hand him over' to a specialist elsewhere. In the event the Centre proved the perfect solution. Mr K was already familiar with it because he'd been there for out-patient appointments.

Out in the open

The Centre, then, enables GPs to extend their medical practice in a variety of ways by providing the appropriate environment to work within and the professional multi-disciplinary team to work with. This multi-disciplinary team is a lot more, though, than another technical resource in the GP's armoury. As someone connected with the Centre — not a doctor — put it, GPs are learning 'to work with a whole lot of people over whom they have no power'. Or, as one of the GPs put it, they're having to come to terms with working in a more exposed way. Their work normally, in homes and in the surgery, is, he said, very private, very individual. Certainly people in the same practice talk when necessary, you consult with health visitors or district nurses or whomever, but you are not accustomed to being watched, let alone judged. Not only is your work in the Centre open to scrutiny, but it is open to scrutiny by fellow-professionals who are as ready to comment and criticise as they are to receive comment and criticism.

It is perfectly possible, said the same GP, to see a patient for whom you have prescribed a particular drug and say, semi-consciously biasing your question, 'Are you feeling better for it?' and to hear 'Yes, I suppose' as meaning that you can forget about that one and turn your attention to the next thing in a busy life. When you see a patient at the Centre and say, 'Are you feeling better?' and he or she replies, 'Yes, I suppose', then the nurse is quite likely to add firmly, 'It may be doing some good, but the pain is not yet anything like as well controlled as it might be. What shall we do about it?' The nurses, the senior ones at least, really do enact their belief that they should be advocates for the patient in this way and the effect on the doctor, said my GP informant, was — once you got used to it — to make you re-examine your practice generally, to sharpen up your awareness of how you were going about your work. Not a comfortable process, of course, and one to which GPs subject themselves in varying degrees.

Practicalities

Another GP who has been probably rather above averagely involved with the Centre took the trouble to work out exactly how much time he had been spending there and in what manner:

> The total time spent with in-patients between 15th July 1985 and 15th July 1986 was 70 hours . . . Today, I saw a patient in the day centre with the community nurse, physio and sister for 15 minutes. I spent a further 30 minutes discussing the management of three other patients with the therapy team. Then I went to see an in-patient for a further 15 minutes. About once a month this amount of time is spent on patient care at the CCC. Over the period of one year a conservative estimate of the time spent discussing patient care in the day centre would be 20 minutes a week . . . The estimate of time spent on patient care during the year is therefore: In-Patients (70 hours) plus day centre (15 hours) — a total of 85 hours. In addition I attended eight audit meetings lasting one hour fifteen minutes giving an additional ten hours approximately. A round figure of 95 hours in 47 weeks, giving an average of about 2 hours a week, would be a conservative estimate of the commitment to the CCC.

Of course, a number of those patients might have been seen at home had the Centre not existed. All the same, being part of a team, nurturing working relationships, attending meetings, all mean extra time to be found. And the contracted GPs are not paid any extra for their work at the Centre (though there have been arrangements for some compensation for doctors taking their turn at serving on, say, the Centre Management Team, which makes a considerable additional call on time beyond what has already been mentioned). So, the medical treatment available at the Centre comes at no extra cost at all to the health service. This initially seemed to me quite right and proper too. However many home visits you make you don't get extra and, in any case, are not doctors already very well paid compared with, for instance, all the other members of the Centre's health-care team? But this chapter has already suggested it is not true that the Centre asks no more of GPs than does their usual practice; it patently does ask more. Additionally, reading about other GP hospitals suggests that it's very rare for doctors not to be paid some sort of special supplement for their work therein, often in the form of a bed allowance.

The GPs associated with the Lambeth Community Care Centre were willing to take on the work for no extra payment, while knowing that other people in other places were being financially rewarded for doing something similar. The 'founding' GPs would certainly have argued that the existence of the Centre was the important thing, that it never occurred to them to stymie the project by standing out for extra payment when there was no money available for it. The Centre was for them so desirable an additional resource that they were glad to support it with extra work. Numbers of them have served faithfully not just in ward and day unit or at the monthly audit meeting, but on the research advisory group or the arts committee or the garden committee or the education committee. Whether or not they *should* be paid, it is clearly worth noting that they are not. And the atmosphere within the Centre is clearly consonant with time and energy given with commitment and without resentment both by the GPs and by all the other more poorly rewarded staff.

Another way in which the Centre differs from the more usual kind of medical institution, though probably not from other GP hospitals, is in having no 'boss', no over-all head, no hierarchy of medical decision-making. The senior nurse is the final arbiter of whether a bed is actually available or not. But imagine that a GP phones about admitting a patient and the senior nurse, or senior nurse on duty, says, no, I really don't think that it sounds appropriate, what then? The theoretical answer is that what follows is referral to the medical referee — a job which the Centre's GPs take on in rotation. The practical answer is that, in fact, such a stark kind of impasse has never yet occurred. It's a credit to the working relationships within the Centre that it hasn't. There are differences of opinion from time to time, but usually amicably resolved. The senior nurse can recall one time when a GP trainee referred a patient and she said — no, I don't think so. But in that case the GP trainee went away to think about it and came back saying, yes, I think after all you're right. So there was no need to call in the referee.

On the three occasions in 18 months when the referee was used, it was always on a friendly basis and not because of any direct confrontation between staff. Once it was a way of getting a GP to move a bit more quickly in making necessary arrangements for a patient's future. Once it was as a double-check when GP and senior nurse both thought that they were probably right to admit a certain patient but were glad of yet another opinion. And the third time he was brought in to help uncross a few wires with a hospital when a patient arrived from hospital on the Centre's doorstep unannounced while both GP and Centre staff were thinking that, though admission had been agreed in principle, it was still some time ahead. Altogether then, the existence of the referee is a necessary safety precaution which, once in place, has not been much used.

What the Centre's existence has signified generally in the lives of local GPs is perhaps best put in the words of one of them: 'It adds a dimension to the work of older doctors and prevents the loss of this dimension for trainee GPs and younger principals.' Or, as another doctor said on a TV programme made about the Centre, 'Mostly it's just opened up a lot of new perspectives in my work.'

6 Taking Risks

> I believe the Centre is important because it not only asks 'why not?', it puts its flexible thinking into flexible practice and, I am convinced, gives the type of care that everyone should be entitled to in all health-care buildings. Admittedly we have healthy staff ratios and a new building but the philosophy still has to be made to happen.
>
> (The administrator)

It might seem somewhat contradictory to start a chapter about risk-taking by considering the role of administration in the Centre. But it's precisely because admin is not traditionally noted as an arm-chancing profession that it's a good place to begin. Also, the administrator has thought a lot about the demands of working there and explains cogently the changes in attitude that she sees as necessary:

> The challenge to the admin department is to think 'why not?' rather than 'why?' in deciding on a course of action. This is not as easy as it sounds. 'Why not?' means you will try because you don't know, which in turn means that you are taking a risk . . . Development has been one of try, see what the pitfalls are and re-write policy . . . as the Centre grows the department grows with it and administrative systems are areas that are always changing.

The administrator (whose department consists of herself, an assistant, a secretary and two porters) admitted that none of this came easily. Being naturally and by professional training cautious, she had had to put quite a lot of effort into maintaining a 'why not?' attitude, compared, for instance, with the senior nurse who had a spontaneous instinct for exactly what kind of risk to take with individual patients and whose natural inclination was to ask 'why on earth not?'

So often, the administrator reflected, things are done in a certain way merely because they've always been done in that way. But the Centre's too small, the sense of being part of a team too powerful to allow you to shut your door on the world and keep your head down in the paperwork. Doors are literally almost always open. Senior staff constantly ask questions about each other's work. Systems — from the most embracing to the most trivial — are discussed at open meetings. One or two files have gone astray; is it personal carelessness, or is the carousel system conducive to misfiling? Should a new filing system be tried?

What it's all for

Being an administrator in such a small unit is quite different from being an administrator on the same grade in a bigger place where you deal with just one little sliver of the work. The Centre stretches its administration in all directions; you are responsible for every aspect of the smooth running of the place. But perhaps most important of all, there's no getting away from patients at the Centre. You can't resort to 'why should we?' when the answer is 'because it might be of benefit to John Smith whom you know'. The administrator is very definite, even while realistic about the effort involved, that the Centre's systems exist *for* the patients. All the necessary paperwork, from clerking in to completing forms after a death, becomes part of the relationship with patients. And patients educate you all the time, either directly — as by telling you in no uncertain terms that they can't talk to you from a wheelchair if you loom over them instead of getting down to the same level for mutual, eye-to-eye conversation — or by the visible paramountcy of their needs.

The manner in which you fulfil the demands of bureaucracy can be in itself therapeutic but there is a further opportunity to feel a part of the health-care team in more direct ways: 'There are numerous examples of admin staff backing up the treatment plans for patients and re-emphasisng the guidance being given by nursing staff.' For one woman in her fifties who was dying:

Our department became part of her treatment plan in organising typing for her to do and obtaining piano music for her to play as she very much needed to do something constructive and feel she was contributing. We all got to know the family and when she did die the porter wanted to go to her funeral as well as the special nurse.

The admin secretary had a particular relationship with another dying patient and would find time each day to stop by for a chat. Then there was the relationship between the assistant administrator and a very anxious patient who phoned more often than his nurse had time to talk to him. The sympathetic interest expressed by the assistant administrator when she fielded the phone calls was such that the patient soon started ringing just to talk to her. This relieved his anxiety without overtaxing nursing staff at busy times. Knowing what advice the patient had been given, the assistant administrator could gently and casually reinforce it.

This might not sound all that risky, but it takes a certain courage and a definite commitment to step out of a clearly defined role, to accept blurring at the edges and to create, thereby, space for trying new things. It would, in fact, be almost impossible to stay behind your role-mask at the Centre.

This openness seems to permeate the place; there isn't anyone on the staff who doesn't see themselves as part of the medical team. If you were to ring up or call in, you'd be pushed to know whether it was the secretary you spoke to or an OT or the senior nurse. If the phone rings, it's answered by whoever's passing. That sounds trivial, I know, but I've worked in lots of places where the common attitude has been 'I'm not going to answer that; it's not for me personally and it'll only make for extra hassle.' Here what goes on is everyone's business. Answering that ringing phone is taking the little risk each time that you'll have to shoulder the responsibility for something rather than waiting for someone else to deal with it.

The motive power for such an attitude comes from an imaginative concentration on the well-being of patients. As one of the two porters said when all the beds were full and there was talk of a young man being admitted to die in the Centre though it hadn't yet been finalised, 'Let's get the spare bed put up now. If

it were me, I'd like to feel that it was ready and waiting for me' —
and never mind the risk that it might turn out to be a little bit of
unnecessary extra work.

Another story of the role that the Centre's porters can play in
the treatment of patients is L's story. L was in her teens (still is)
and had had her leg so badly damaged in an accident that
amputation was considered. When she came home from the
hospital orthopaedic department she was not only unable to walk
but also very demoralised and lacking in the confidence or will to
try. She lived, fortunately, near to the Centre. She would not
trust herself with strangers, didn't want to go in an ambulance,
but was willing to go to the Centre for physiotherapy if collected
by Centre staff whom she already knew from home visits. At first
a physiotherapist used to go round with one of the porters to
fetch her by wheelchair. L then developed considerable faith in
the porter and he used to go to call for her every day, first with
the wheelchair and later to walk beside her while she made her
first short journeys on crutches. Her confidence in him was
clearly a factor in her new willingness to try to become mobile.
So he would start his shift earlier than he was due in order not to
let her down.

All the staff then are in some way directly involved with
patients, unable, even if they wanted to, to lose touch with the
essential reasons for what they do. There are also those people
who, while not employed at the Centre, have regular working
links with it. I'm thinking particularly of the London Ambulance
Service. The men who bring patients in to out-patient
appointments and to the day unit are in their way a part of the
health-care team, too. It's not the most exciting of jobs, the
daily run to pick people up and deliver them to the Centre. One
crew used to be assigned to this duty all the time but now there
are rotating crews, doing one week out of six working with the
Centre. But they, too, are willing to go beyond the bare
requirements of the job. In the worst of the 1987 winter's cold,
the sister on the day unit said that she had no fears for any of the
Centre's regular patients because the ambulance crews were
going into every home in order to check that people had
sufficient warmth and were properly looked after. When older
people who lived alone said that they were afraid to go out in the
snow, the crews made considerable efforts to persuade them that

the journey would not be at all difficult and that they would be better off in the Centre.

The business of taking risks goes along with taking responsibility and with working closely with colleagues; and they all stem from a concern for the patient.

Guidelines

Of course, when the Centre was set up, its own position had to be fairly clearly demarcated. Since it was taking up territory within the District Health Authority that hadn't been staked out before, it was important both for the people who were to work there and for others in the DHA that the perimeters of that territory be clear and agreed.

The Centre's founding guidelines existed both to delineate its function, showing that it would not encroach on ground already covered elsewhere, and to protect Centre staff against unworkable demands.

Categories of patient originally excluded were:
- people requiring specialist care
- people under 16 years old
- people with notifiable infectious diseases
- people with acute psychiatric disorders

And there was the length-of-stay maximum of 28 days in order to guard against the place insidiously turning into a long-stay ward.

Patients in need of specialist care never will be admitted to the Centre. Overlap would be wasteful when specialist services are available at three nearby teaching hospitals. Nor are there any plans at the moment to take younger patients. The senior nurse occasionally gets that 'why not?' gleam in her eye — why not if they come from local families, don't need specialist care and a single room is available? But, so far, that guideline remains inviolate and the general view is that the Centre is not geared to the needs of children as patients.

All the other guidelines have now been departed from on occasion. This does not mean that they are unnecessary, merely that they are guidelines and not tablets of the law. Their existence has been important in safeguarding the particular ethos and character of the Centre.

Take the 28-day limit on stay. This was crucial for the preservation of the Centre's nature as a dynamic place of primary medical care fostering patients' own autonomy. Many patients are elderly and, indeed, one or two have used their time in the Centre to come to terms with the fact that they cannot manage alone any longer and will have to move to some kind of long-term care. But most have become re-energised for independent local life. With only 20 beds in the Centre, had GPs succumbed to the temptation to let people stay on without any plan for treatment and revitalisation, then the Centre would have found its nature much altered. Admission has been deflected when it has been clear that long-term care is needed and that a stay at the Centre would serve no function other than to delay the making of proper arrangements. This refusal is legitimated by the length-of-stay guideline. There is a great need, of course, for civilised long-term care facilities, but that is not what the Centre is for.

Because of the confidence engendered by the guideline, it can now readily be contravened in letter while the spirit remains intact. It is broken when serious discussion between GP and staff leads to the conclusion that, as in the case of Miss A, a person may genuinely get on to his/her feet again by means of a rehabilitative programme which takes longer than a month.

The other guidelines were also for the Centre's own protection and have now been occasionally set aside. This has never been through trying to deal with what is better left to the general hospital, but always because of some particular circumstance which made the Centre seem especially relevant. There is still no intention to take patients primarily because they have infectious illnesses; there are other places better equipped. In the case of Mr H, however, with whom suspicion of an infectious disease arose when he was already an in-patient with a rehabilitative programme planned, there was careful deliberation but no invoking of the guideline as a totem. Other factors were thought more important. And he stayed, was barrier nursed, recovered and no one else got hepatitis.

Similarly, with another patient who had a brief paranoid episode linked with physical illness and took to chasing imaginary people through the greenhouse, there was no use of the rule-book. Common-sense discussion and a move into a single bedroom sufficed and the episode soon passed.

New departure

It's one thing to accept a technical departure from the guidelines for a patient already in the Centre, another to set them aside at the very start of the admission. The first specifically psychiatric admission was a cause, then, of some trepidation. It happened when staff were confident that the nature of the Centre was well established and only after a great deal of discussion of plans and possible repercussions.

The way that it came about was this. A local GP was visited by a woman he knew who wanted to talk about her husband whom he did not then know although the man was registered with his practice. The husband was at the time in a psychiatric ward in a south London hosptial (it was not his first admission to mental hospital). Their marriage was in some difficulties but the fact that they could no longer live together didn't mean that Mrs M didn't care about what happened to her husband. She was frustrated because she felt that she had no voice in plans for his future, and couldn't get to talk to his doctors. She was also perturbed because Mr M, who had first been diagnosed as schizophrenic in 1978, was quite heavily drugged with largactil and modecate and yet there was talk of discharging him, unsupported, to bed-and-breakfast accommodation across the river.

The GP talked with Mr M's hospital doctors and heard their view of the situation. He gathered from them that they were not even sure that the original diagnosis was correct. But the hospital was indeed proposing the B&B option. Since this didn't seem very promising for Mr M's future, the GP talked to the senior nurse about the possibility of admitting Mr M to the Centre with a view to reducing his medication under supervision so that a clearer picture might emerge of what he was actually like. It would also provide the opportunity for further conversation about his future plans in which his wife could be involved. Mr M was known to be unaggressive and co-operative. Also, importantly, the psychiatric specialists were willing to go along with this scheme and offer back-up if necessary. Altogether, there were quite a number of guarantees that the admission would not adversely affect the Centre or any of its other patients.

All the same, the staff were nervous. Nervous, they thought afterwards, of the label. None of them is psychiatrically trained and that made them a bit uncertain about their approach at first — for about three or four days, they reckoned. Good communications among the staff were useful in ensuring that knowledge was pooled. The fact that Mr M tended to say different things to different people didn't matter because they were all aware of the variations. Where he wavered most was in whether he did or didn't want to get better.

Since, if left, Mr M would have slept each day away, some sort of therapy seemed essential. The OTs were thinking on their feet because there was no obvious single activity to hand — no need for physical rehabilitation and pointless to introduce something which had no rationale other than to keep Mr M busy. So they decided to concentrate on relaxation and on social skills. His key worker OT introduced a daily programme of relaxation exercises, reduced to three sessions a week with her once Mr M had the hang of it well enough to carry on by himself on the other days. Meantime, he was drawn into doing small things for other patients, being asked to take round tea or whatever. At first it was a question of always remembering to ask him because he hadn't the energy to see things for himself but responded well to requests.

All the time his drugs were being reduced. The modecate injections were stopped. The largactil was eased off gradually until, by the time he left the Centre, he was down from 3×300 mg. a day to 1×100. He was much more alert and appeared to suffer no ill effects.

Although there was no question of his going back to live with his wife, he was able to visit his family who lived nearby and they were able to pop in to see him. Mrs M felt that she had a real role in helping him towards a future with possibilities in it. A social worker outside the Centre had already been involved with Mr M so his GP and the OT liaised with her, particularly about where Mr M should go when it seemed he was ready to move on. In the end, he was discharged to one of the Richmond Fellowship's rehabilitative homes. When he dropped in at the Centre at Christmas time to say hello, he also said that he liked it there and would be staying (he hadn't been 100 per cent sure when the idea was first mooted).

When it came to discussion at an audit meeting of the appropriateness of Mr M's stay at the Centre there was agreement that it had been thoroughly successful. It was a vital intervention because if there'd been nothing available between discharge from the psychiatric ward and the projected B&B loneliness, then it was possible Mr M would have started that drifting downward spiral into less and less hope, a route which can have destitution or vagrancy at its end.

Mr M's story suggests that there is a role for the small, non-specialist unit in the care of some people with mental illnesses. Among the features of the Centre identified by staff as having contributed to Mr M's recovery of energy and interest and a measure of control of his own life were its smallness and the very fact that it was not a psychiatric unit. (I would also add the quality of individual care offered by GP and staff.)

The main focus of the post-admission discussion, though, was on the relationship of this admission to the Centre's guidelines. It had been a risk. It had worked. But did it suggest the new risk of opening floodgates to torrents of requests for similar admissions? Were this to be so, all agreed, then in a hypothetical ideal world the answer would be more such Centres, never, ever the expansion of this one. That would quite destroy its effectiveness.

A glance through the records suggests, though, that every time there's been a new type of admission similar fears have been expressed and never yet fulfilled. It's a natural worry, all the same, springing from a communal protectiveness of the Centre's nature, of the core of safety which makes it possible to take the risks.

By coincidence the same audit meeting which ruminated over Mr M's admission, also considered the treatment of Mr N, a man in his eighties who had gradually acquired more and more signs of ill-health and more and more treatments for those signs: Parkinsonian tremors, urinary problems, enlarged prostate, depression (since the death of his wife in 1979). By the time he was admitted to the Centre, he was low in body and spirit, withdrawn, shaky, weak and unsteady on his feet. Nothing that the Centre staff did seemed to effect any improvement so a visit from a consultant geriatrician was requested. The geriatrician recommmended that ultra-sound be tried for Mr N's painful symptoms and that all medication of all kinds be stopped. The Centre staff and GP did as suggested and waited, with some anxiety. Within three or four days Mr N's mood began to improve and his walking to become steadier. He went home just before Christmas and when rung up in January to see how he was getting on said he was fine and sounded it.

Lots of problems are caused by treatments, said one GP ruefully after the meeting. But again the Centre provides the sheltered environment, as it did with Mr K, in which the risk of withdrawing medication, often very long-established medication, can be taken. It might not be possible to justify the use of an acute bed in the DGH for the purpose nor could it readily be chanced with the patient still at home. It needs monitoring. Had there been an adverse reaction instead of an increase in the patient's well-being in each case, then practised assessment and readily available medical response would have been vital.

These few examples must stand for an attitude which is pervasive in the Centre, whether it manifests itself in assisting a patient to go out to the pictures or in sharing feelings with colleagues or in taking a quick decision. The senior nurse says that if she had to pass on in a nutshell the qualities most crucial to the Centre's character she would choose the inter-linked trio of emphasis on patient-autonomy, the nurse's role as advocate for the patient and the willingness to take risks.

7 Renewal

I am amazed at my degree of recovery and I am more than
grateful to all at the Community Care Centre.

(CVA patient)

'No one's to be given up on' is a sentiment that I heard expressed
more than once in differing ways by various members of staff,
thinking aloud about their individual work or talking in a group
about patients who seemed to have made no progress.

There may at first sight appear to be something of a
contradiction between the encouraging of patient autonomy and
the need not to let that autonomy express itself in giving up.
What if a patient's most real desire is not to get better, to be ill
and be looked after? Staff would reply, I imagine, that an
inclination to give up on life is often the result of fear and
insecurity. So, if the Centre can help a patient to feel safe, then
that patient will naturally begin to feel like standing on her or his
own feet again. It's just that sometimes it takes longer than
others.

Making the most of things
This theme of coming to feel secure enough to attempt new
things — be it walking, taking care of yourself, making friends,
wanting to go home — has been implicit in earlier chapters. It's
there in all the work on the ward. From the moment of
admission there is a consciousness of the patient's possible future.

It's in the day unit, though, that the primacy of rehabilitative
work is most clearly seen. Whether there for a half-an-hour
appointment or all-day attendance, the day unit's patients are

learning in some way to maximise the capacities that they have, even if this means adjusting to living with a degree of disability.

As remarked earlier, the readily available physiotherapy has been used a lot. For a young, active, possibly working person, the Centre offers quick help in returning to normal. A trainee GP said of the Centre's service, 'The vast majority of my referrals were to the physios at the day hospital with acute back, shoulder and neck problems . . . I rapidly found that patients got much more relief (from frozen shoulders) by a combination of early physio with analgesia.' Over and again GPs made similar comments on the fact that people are speedily relieved of the pain of soft tissue injuries at the Centre whereas before they might have had to spend weeks of incapacity waiting for a hospital appointment.

The Centre's records suggest not only that there is a great deal of soft tissue injury around but that some groups and professions are more prone to it than others. Dustmen are subject to bad backs, window-cleaners and bus-conductors are vulnerable to the effects of sudden movement, twisting or jarring and joggers present regularly with leg injuries.

Another GP told of a labourer with severe lower back strain who was able to return to work within three weeks after immediate out-patient physiotherapy. He continued going to the Centre, though, to the 'back school' at which the Centre's physios teach groups of people with a tendency to back strain how best to stand and sit and move and lift and carry in order to avoid such strain in future. In the case of a teenage girl who was getting worrying pain in her hands just before she was due to sit exams, the Centre provided swift physiotherapy, a supportive splint (from the OT department) and a degree of general reassurance. Her GP felt that, had she had to wait for a hospital out-patient appointment, her anxiety would have been greatly increased and her performance in the exams, which in the event she was able to sit normally, at risk.

Yet another GP spoke of a window-cleaner who fell from a ledge and injured his back. The pain was not much reduced by bed rest alone but after four sessions of physio he was ready to go back to his windows. And then there was the typical young jogger with ham-string strain who was treated with ice packs and ultra-sound and was discharged in less than a fortnight, with lots of good advice about how to warm up properly, ready to go back to active sport.

The range of assessments and treatments that the physios, in conjunction with the OTs, can offer to GP and patient has been listed by the senior physiotherapist as including: provision of walking aids, collars, corsets and splints; musculoskeletal assessments for GPs; gait assessments for GPs; home-visit assessments; regular, long-term planned review of patients, e.g. with neurological problems; liaison with the community services in the treatment of, e.g. ulcers; assessment of elderly patients with multi-fractural problems; out-patient chest physiotherapy; continued care of amputees after surgery; involvement with gynaecological problems; orthopaedic referrals for a progressive rehabilitative programme; involvement with other staff with the chronically and terminally ill; acupuncture. And, of course, pain-control measures like the use of ultra-sound and educational measures like the back school, offering prophylactic care to patients and to fellow-staff with advice on such things as the correct ways of lifting.

If you look at the out-patient therapy available at the Centre from the GP's point-of-view it's a very useful extra resource; from the patient's point-of-view it's a quick, local, unalarming and effective service; from the point-of-view of the big hospitals, the health service and even the state, it's an economical provision, removing some of the burden from hospital waiting lists and reducing working days lost through injury.

The story of Mr O illustrates a number of aspects of the work of Centre's physios — and, as is almost inevitable except with the very simplest of referrals, of the multi-disciplinary team generally. The senior physio describes his progress from first referral at the age 61 with muscular atrophy.

> Mr O was walking with elbow crutches and the physios and OTs have suggested adaptations and different walking aids to enable Mr O to walk more safely, comfortably and less tiredly. An assessment of his physical capabilities was made at the Centre, to give an accurate picture and also as a report which could be used in future. This enabled Mr O to be instructed to be as functionally independent as he could physically manage at that time. A home visit was made by

physio and OT to determine how Mr O managed to get out of his flat and to the local shops. This gave an accurate picture of Mr O's exercise tolerance and local situation, so that we could instruct Mr O with appropriate advice.

An assessment was made at the Centre by physio and OT of the strength, range of movement and functional capabilities of Mr O's arms and hands. This was followed up by a home visit assessment to determine related problems at home. Thus we were able to suggest particularly appropriate aids and adapt treatment accordingly.

Because of an infected toe

Mr O was seen by the chiropodist and nursing staff at the Centre who were able to clean, debride and dress the infected area. Mr O was then given support to remove pressure from his shoe by the chiropodist and instructed how best to walk by the physio, As Mr O was further admitted to St Thomas's for removal of the toe nail, the Centre has since been involved in liaising with the district nurse in arranging dressings.

Mr O has a chronic chest problem, resulting in shortness of breath. The Centre has also liaised with the chest clinic Mr O attends and also in recording Mr O's exercise to correlate this with physio treatment.

Since Mr O retired he has been unable to develop an active role within his family and has few interests and hobbies. The physios and OTs are offering him opportunities to increase his interest within his physical capabilities.

Recovering from a stroke

One area in which this kind of quickly available, co-ordinated rehabilitative care can be particularly useful is with patients who've had strokes. The Centre staff have been concerned enough with how to relieve the after-effects of cardio-vascular accidents to devote two of their precious audit meetings to this theme. A discussion of the wisdom of admitting to the ward patients who'd just had strokes was followed a few months later by an invitation to a specialist to come and talk about what factors to look out for in treating a CVA patient and how to predict what could be expected by way of recovery of function.

Although this advice was being taken precisely because GPs were at that stage still cautious about direct admission to the ward immediately following a stroke, the day unit has from the start undertaken rehabilitative work with patients after strokes. One of the Centre's earliest out-patients (the same patient who described the official opening) has written his own account of the care he was offered at the Centre.

By now my right arm and hand and my right leg were fairly useless. I could not grip a knife or spoon; writing was impossible and I could not walk without a helping arm and a walking stick. Going up and down stairs and getting into bed were considerable problems.

On Thursday I was collected by ambulance and taken to the Care Centre. Here I was given a warm welcome (and an unexpected lunch) by the sister and then handed over to the physiotherapist. She spent an hour assessing the extent of the effects after the stroke and arranged that I came for exercises every afternoon in the coming week. No time wasted . . .

The following week the ambulance collected me each afternoon and I was put through a series of exercises. These included lifting weights with my right arm, exercising my right leg, pedalling on an exercise bicycle and attempting to get up and down a flight of stairs.

In addition, the occupational therapist tested the ability of my fingers to locate small foreign objects in a bowl of split lentils and encouraged me to use pen and paintbrush.

By the end of the first week I was amazed at my degree of recovery. My right hand had regained a large degree of its original grip although after five minutes of writing the words became smaller and smaller. I found that I could now lift a tea cup and even a beer mug with some confidence.

Walking without the aid of a stick was becoming almost a possibility. I could get in and out of bed unaided and getting shaved, washed and dressed was no longer a serious problem.

During the second week my walking ability was further tested. It befell thus; there emerged from the Centre a small procession — myself flanked on each side by physio and OT and followed, as chaperone, by a red-haried young man pushing a wheelchair. Marching fairly steadily, if slowly, I realised we had reached Kennington Road. Without a word of warning the OT announced that we would catch a bus! Up came a number 159; we three leapt on board leaving red-hair behind. At the next stop we de-bussed none the worse . . . Rejoining the wheelchair I was glad of a short ride but completed the last lap back to the Centre on my own legs.

This had overcome my reluctance to walk abroad. But enough for one day. It was now Thursday afternoon. I do not return to the Centre until next Tuesday. I drew up a chart to record my daily exercises at home and planned a minimum of one walk a day outdoors . . .

On my next visit to the Centre, the exercises with my leg and the cycling were followed by trying to stand on the 'Wobble-Board'. This is a board fixed to a horizontal cylinder. To achieve the 'delicate balance' was extremely difficult but challenging . . .

The next day I made a further attempt to regain normalcy. A classmate took me by car to the Morley College to my English Literature class. It was good to be back again. I came away at the coffee break. It was long enough for the first time . . .

Friday, I walked unaided for 15 minutes outdoors this morning. At the Centre it was, for me, D (Discharge) Day. For the last time I was collected and returned home by ambulance.

What a difference in the way I can now walk and use my limbs compared with four weeks ago . . .

Complementary skills

It's clear from that account that physios and OTs work very closely together (and, had the patient needed speech therapy, that too would have been on offer). The ready availability of occupational therapy as one of a GP's treatment options is perhaps even more unusual than easy direct access to physio.

Sometimes, in a hospital, an OT's own options are limited by the fact that she may cover as many as eight wards and have time to do little more than respond to the consultant's desire to get people moving as quickly as possible. On the other hand, there are community occupational therapists helping people to adapt to living in their own homes but, since they work mainly with social-work departments, what they can do is not all that familiar to GPs.

So, the Centre's three OTs are in a unique position to bridge the hospital/community gap and to make the full range of their services not only available but more familiar to other members of the primary health-care team. And just what are these services? Well, as already seen, they work very well in tandem with physios, sometimes using complementary skills on the same damaged limb or impaired function (witness the patient with a stroke learning with the OT to pick up small objects again). OTs and physios do a great many joint home visits, using their different approaches to the observation of an environment to build a complete picture of what is and what is not possible for the patient. While the physio may then be able to show someone how best to use his or her own strengths to negotiate the awkward steps, the OT may be able to get a handrail fixed to make the process easier, just as she may be able to provide the aids that make taking a bath possible or putting on a pair of tights when you can't bend and your hands are stiff with arthritis.

Within the Centre, the occupational therapy department has the facilities to help patients to learn, or re-learn after illness or injury, how to do necessary tasks, like shopping and cooking. For an elderly man, recently widowed, not very fit, completely unused to 'doing' for himself, simply going out to buy a boil-in-the-bag kipper and heating it up in the Centre kitchen may be quite an achievement. The OT and the dietician sometimes work together in the kitchen to sort out with a patient the 'what' as well as the 'how' of cooking.

The OTs are also, of course, the makers of splints and other physical supports for damaged limbs. Their techniques are not, however, limited to assisting patients with physical adaptation to their environment. When the physios are helping to reduce someone's pain with ultra-sound and relevant exercises, the OTs may well be working with the same patient to help them to relax — 'relaxation techniques continue the idea that the patient has a certain amount of control over his/her own symptoms'. They have found such techniques beneficial for patients with cancer, asthma, migraine or other kinds of intractable pain. Sometimes the OTs' teaching of physical relaxation goes along with the use of acupuncture by the physios and both may be accompanied by education in the control and reduction of stress generally.

The nurses who have worked in the day unit have also seen their role as part of the communal rehabilitative effort, offering counselling and encouraging the development of social skills in patients who have become rather isolated.

The story of Mrs P is a very good illustration of how therapy and nursing go together. Mrs P was originally referred for physiotherapy because she had a very painful episiotomy scar after the birth of her first child. The physios treated the scar itself with ultra-sound and also showed Mrs P how she could gently stretch the scar tissue and how she could, for the time being, most comfortably sit. During the course of this treatment, Mrs P's other concerns gradually emerged. She got advice from both the physio and the dietician about the constipation which aggravated the pain of the scar and she was slowly able to talk about other related personal problems. She had also been rather unsure about her mothering.

> She felt able to leave her baby in the day unit during her treatment sessions, enabling her to relax more. She often sought advice from fellow patients who were experienced mothers, grandmothers and great-grandmothers about behavioural problems with her child. She found it extremely convenient to have access to the canteen, kitchen, sitting room and garden — it gave her a welcome break from her small flat . . .

so said one of the sisters, but the senior physiotherapist paid more direct tribute to the nurses' involvement: 'she was developing handling skills by discussion and demonstration from the nurses'.

It was agreed by both nurses and therapists that Mrs P was an excellent example of the kind of patient who could benefit from the Centre's multi-disciplinary approach, from its friendly informality and from the fact that it is possible to be there for much longer than the actual time of out-patient appointments. She left not only in less pain but more relaxed and less isolated and worried than when she arrived. Sometimes, as in Mrs P's case, this kind of multi-faceted relationship with the day-unit team follows a referral for one specific problem. On other occasions, it depends on the GP spotting the possible usefulness to a patient of all-day admission to the day unit — or a hospital doctor or nurse doing so and passing the suggestion on.

A day at a time

When a patient is being discharged from a general hospital, doesn't need further in-patient treatment but would clearly benefit from some sort of further help in coping with the after-effects of what took them to the general hospital in the first place, then the day unit is a fairly obvious thought. Teenager L, with her badly damaged leg 'after tragic reckless driving by a motor cyclist', is a good case in point.

> Her morale was very low . . . she had become dependent on her parents . . . Gradually, with *much* work, continuity of care and team approach (GP, DN, physio and nurse) in an open, honest relationship, she began to respond and trust us. She eventually began walking again. She has had more surgery and still more to come; she always invites us to attend out-patients at St Thomas' with her so that we are all in the picture. If there is a problem she rings up and one of us goes round if it is serious. We have had many meetings with her GP, DN, physio, OT, L and her parents to discuss plans and difficulties. Her parents occasionally call into the Centre if something is bothering them.

Such a referral can equally well be made from home if a GP picks up on a patient's need for some general day-time support with nursing care and therapy. Day-unit attendance is often particularly helpful for patients whose physical problems are exacerbated by their being alone and becoming frightened or depressed.

> Very elderly lady with chronic and severe leg ulceration; despite regular care from district nurses showed little improvement and was becoming increasingly depressed. Referred to the LCCC for day care with marked improve-

ment in leg ulceration and general mental state. Would have been inappropriate to refer to hospital. Now dis-charged to own home. Also had opportunity for visits by chiropodist, dentist and OT help for arthritis.

Services available in the day unit are being constantly evaluated, like all the Centre's work, and expanded. A recent development which looks likely to take off in various directions is the extension of one-to-one therapy into related groups for patients who have some problems in common. There are group activities which are directly educational, like the back school. The OTs' tuition in stress management is offered to groups as well as individuals. And then there are the less structured mutual support groups. We've seen earlier how the group for people with neurological problems — 'the Backing Group' — was started by the OTs (with the rehabilitation adviser from the local social services area office) but then became self-perpetuating. Having observed how very useful such groups can be, some of the staff are currently particularly interested in doing more by way of facilitating the setting up of groups. The community link worker, the OTs, some of the nurses and the social worker are all keen to become further involved in group work.

Group work is a way of helping people to help themselves and it's also a way of making more links between the Centre and the surrounding community, involving people in health care *before* they need particular medical help. Having been on a training course run by the local health education department, the community link worker has been able to start a series of weekly 'Look After Yourself!' sessions, open to anyone, at which people share their ideas about health as well as learning how to stay as healthy as possible. Other groups starting up on the Centre's premises include one for people who have recently been bereaved. An Al-Anon group uses the Centre for meetings and lately, by their own request, a group of mothers with small babies has begun to meet regularly there.

Such groups are wholly consonant with a policy of en-couraging patient (and potential patient) independence. Although a number of the staff are more than willing to be involved in the setting up of groups, they see themselves as facilitators rather than leaders. As they say in an illustrated pamphlet about the Centre produced in spring 1987, 'Support groups are defined by our "community" of users and set up in response to need rather than at our instigation.'

So far, so lively. There are exciting prospects of the continued pushing out of the boundaries of what the Centre can do to help people to grasp their own health, their own lives. People have obtained speedy help with injury, confidence-giving help after they've been set back by major illness or accident, morale-boosting help if they've become isolated, miserable and self-neglectful. Even the inexpensive hair-dressing available at the Centre once a week plays its part.

Problems

However, the day unit has not been problem-free. There is always going to be some aspect of the Centre's life coming in for communal scrutiny (the time to worry will be when that stops and everything is taken for granted). In the relatively brief time which I spent around the Centre, it happened to be the turn of the day unit for serious examination. There were discussions at meetings about problems right through the Centre — discharge letters not being written quickly enough, lost files, dirty cups being left for someone else to wash up, security of the premises at night (with just two nurses on duty) — but when it came to the day unit it was major questions about how the Centre could be true to its special vision which were surfacing.

It is perhaps not startling that the day unit should be the area to illumine continuing questions. Compared with that of the ward, its work is sprawling, multifarious and not neatly contained. GPs are at ease with ward referral, at ease with out-patient referral, but Centre staff still feel that not all GPs are sure what all-day attendance at the day unit is for. This is becoming less and less true over time, as more and more GPs begin to use the day unit, but the initial lack of certainty may have reflected some uncertainties within the Centre itself.

At team meetings in early 1987 anxieties were voiced about the relationship between the ward and the day unit. All nursing staff were at that time required to serve in both in order that the work of the Centre should remain essentially unified. Since, however, the needs of the 24-hour-a-day ward are greater, nurses worked for comparatively brief periods in the day unit. There was sometimes a subtle temptation, other members of staff thought, for nurses, in spite of the opportunities to become involved in counselling and group work, to look on work in the day unit, with its nine-to-five routine, as second-best nursing.

Nurses themselves were aware of a problem in relating day-unit work to ward work but saw it more in terms of lack of good communications between the two. Nurses who were then working on the day unit felt that they did not always get proper briefing from the ward when a patient moved from in-patient care to day care. Nurses who were about to go down to the day unit for the first time felt that they did not know enough about what would be expected of them there. Altogether there was a sense of a more than desirable separation between ward and day unit — but this was beginning to exercise staff, to be seen as a major problem to be remedied.

There were also some problems of communication within the day unit itself. There had been a slightly confusing system whereby each day patient had a named nurse-carer who might also be that patient's key worker. However, a good number of day patients had as their key worker, responsible for co-ordinating their treatment, one of the therapists. And they were finding that a few patients had been left without a key worker at all because somehow the responsibility just hadn't been allocated. One team meeting I went to spent its time devising a new rota system for receiving all general referrals and seeing that they were immediately allocated to the most likely looking key worker.

There were, however, more subtle problems arising from differences in attitudes which hadn't always been acknowledged or even consciously recognised. One such difference could loosely be described as a difference between a nursing and a therapeutic approach, though not, of course, as clearly portioned out between people as that description suggests.

The day unit is a medical unit; it is not a social day centre. The reasons for a person to be there are primarily health ones. A patient may need multiple therapies and therefore be around for long stretches of the day or they may need encouragement to regain the confidence and energy to attend to personal hygiene or nutrition or other kinds of self-care. But the general aim is to stimulate the patient to move on into independence of the day unit. If the only remaining unfulfilled need is for company during the day, then staff will help the patient seek out another, socially-based day centre where they can go permanently.

While there is agreement on this basic stance, differences of opinion exist about how much, how soon and how fast. Some staff are prone to emphasise the importance of visible forward movement and others to insist that not giving up on anyone may well include giving them a very great deal of time.

Thanks to the insistence of the senior nurse, four day-unit places are now kept for longer staying patients (that means more than four people since some come for only one or two days a week). Her view is that the actual circumstances and need of the patient ought never to be forgotten and that discharge dates should not be arranged too firmly in advance, a practice conducive to loss of sight of the patient's present needs. For some people the ability to try a little requires a very large amount of prior safety and support. Nor is the line between health and social need that easy to draw. There are people who have medical problems which would prevent their attendance at another, less medically-geared day centre and who might, without quite long-term support from the Centre, make yet more demands on the health service.

An old woman who is, at the time of writing, happy and quiet within the day unit and quiet at home at night had been, when left to her own devices at home, rather prone to screaming during both day and night. The neighbours were so pleased by the change in her when she started going to the Centre that they said they'd even be willing to pay for a taxi to take her there. In the view of the senior nurse, if it were not for the day unit, either the patient would end up on a geriatric ward or her son (who lived with her but was at work all day) would need psychiatric help. But this view met some resistance from those who believed that the Centre should never be a place of containment without the prospect of further movement by the patient towards autonomy and independence.

Another, apparently paradoxical observation made of the day unit around this time was that it did too much containing and not nearly enough encouraging of patient autonomy. One of my own early impressions, perhaps because the sitting room is so visible within its lozenge of glass walls in the entrance area, was that there were stretches of the day when patients seemed to just sit, all rather formally grouped within a small space. Of course 'just sitting' can be important. People need to rest between therapy appointments. They may need to chat to one another in a very desultory and unforced way as part of their experiment in sociability. The position of the sitting room, which I had originally thought too public, is actually very good for helping patients to feel at the hub of things, seeing all the comings and goings — woe betide the GP who tries to sneak by unnoticed! And yet there was some of that look about it of day rooms everywhere, an air of waiting rather than of being and doing.

Staff were themselves beginning to articulate a feeling that the possibilities of the day unit, as a place to *be* all day, had not been fully explored or used. There seemed, oddly, to be less patient autonomy here than in the ward. It's easier in the ward, of course; mobile patients can choose between their own rooms, the sitting room, the corridor seats, the verandahs, the greenhouse and the kitchen where they can make themselves a cup of tea any time. The day unit, by comparison, seemed more limited physically. True I was seeing it in winter and, by all accounts, it spills and spreads over the patio and garden in summer as patients wander out through the open French doors and meals are taken al fresco.

Within the glass room different things to do, like the large jigsaw in one corner, were beginning to appear as staff turned their attention to this problem of giving day patients freedom of choice. There have always been frequent social events, the celebration of a birthday or a discussion or a demonstration, and the entrance hall is always full of small ads — 'piano player wanted' or 'art teacher sought'. Yet the day-unit problem was reflected in the fact that such events became, by default, almost compulsory. The unit didn't somehow provide the space within which to be independent and pass up on those activities which didn't appeal to you. When there were no arranged activities going on patients tended to stay put, awaiting what came next. And small changes weren't getting to the root question of how to enable day patients to be more independent.

Changes
The answer proved to be quite simple if unexpected and involved

a sideways look at something which had come to seem almost axiomatic — the rotation of nurses through ward and day unit and the numbers of nursing staff needed in the day unit. Although the alternation of sisters between ward and day unit had been intended to prevent the development of separate domains, the two had remained all the same somewhat separate. Also, the presence of a sister and two or three other nurses within the day unit meant that they were being turned to as the organisers of the patients' days. The resignation of a sister for domestic reasons coincided with a serious consideration of the day unit's problems by staff and by the senior nurse in particular. The result was the removal from the day unit of all nursing staff except for the new sister (now one of three sisters with the ward's complement increased to two).

The results of this change were remarkable in terms of answering at a stroke several of the problems described in this chapter. One nurse could not be expected to do all the necessary physical caring for all the patients. So those patients who have previously been on the ward now keep the same special nurses they had as in-patients. The special nurse comes down to deal with any particular treatment her patient needs, while the day-unit sister keeps a general eye on things and treats those patients who have had no previous links with the Centre.

This arrangement means that complaints about lack of proper handover and passage of information have become irrelevant since any patient progressing through the Centre will have the same special nurse throughout. It also means that the separation between ward and day unit is beginning to crumble as nurses come and go between the two on a daily basis and day patients feel free to roam, popping upstairs to find their nurse if they want her.

Also, and dramatically, it has changed the atmosphere of the day unit from one of waiting to one of activity and choice. Because it is clear that one nurse cannot run everything and everyone, the patients now see it as their responsibility to organise themselves with the result that much more is happening. Rather than sitting and looking at one another, they are much freer of the Centre as a whole and scatter into a variety of activities, exercising choices about whether to go off alone or to be with people and talk, whether to get together to arrange a communal social event or to spend the time in some quiet, reflective or creative activity.

It's early days yet. The changed system has only been in operation for a few weeks at the time of writing. But the alteration of organisational structure has proved instantly effective because it was based on a fundamental look at how the things that were worrying people related to the Centre's whole philosophy of health care. The results are very promising for the future development of the day unit as a different kind of place to be, opening up new prospects for patients, often at a time when their lives looked like becoming narrowed by ill-health. Add this newly enlarged atmosphere to the medical rehabilitation so freely offered by the whole team and the Centre looks set to become, as a whole, a place where it is safe to try again, to experiment even and discover new possibilities in yourself.

8 Respite

> I came to the Centre with a bad chest for the first time last winter. I find it a struggle to manage sometimes but I can and I want to live in my own home.
>
> (Patient, aged 94)

> Since her first admission with congestive cardiac failure we offered Maggie one week in six regular respite care. This has been very successful in keeping her fitter and keeping her spirits up.
>
> (Nurse)

One of the things that the Centre does with its own money (money raised by ex-patients and other friendly volunteers at jumble sales and the like) is to pay, since it cannot offer the service itself, for respite care elsewhere for a local child with spina bifida. This gives the parents short, restorative breaks from their intensive responsibility.

That suggests the value that staff place on respite care after their experience of making it available for adult patients. Four of the beds are, more or less, kept for chronically ill or handicapped people who come in from time to time to give them a rest from struggling on alone or to give the people who care for them a rest. Emergency respite care can also be provided if a carer should be taken suddenly ill.

The need
You have only to consider the situations of some of the families known to local GPs to realise what an enormous need there is for

this sort of medical support. It's all very well for politicians of a certain stamp to suggest that burdens on state services would be much reduced if only families would shoulder their own responsibilities, but how many of them have ever had the sole care of a multiply handicapped relative for year after year?

The problems that one of the sisters describes in connection with Mrs Q and her family are not all that uncommon:

> A splendid old lady of 78 who had a severe stroke seven years ago, she is incontinent, unable to speak, feed herself, immobile and wheel-chair bound. Amazingly her family look after her, mainly her brother (81) and her daughter who works full-time. She came to us in a moment of crisis for nursing care. After much discussion with the family, GP, district nurse, the home situation was clearly becoming strained due to Mrs Q's rather demented husband who also needed care. We decided to support them with holiday care and twice weekly visits to the day unit for baths and nursing care. Without the Centre's input undoubtedly Mrs Q would now be in long-term care; this would be sad as the family are committed to looking after her. We review the situation regularly with home visits and update care as necessary.

Respite care, as is evident from this account, is not offered in a vacuum but as part of the Centre's total service which will include home visits and may include use of the day unit.

It would have been sad for Mrs Q and her family if she had had to go into long-term care for lack of sufficient support when they actually wanted to stay together. It would also have been more expensive, a charge on the state coffers much greater than a minute portion of the Centre's total costs and a fraction of the district nurse's salary. The economic value of the Centre cannot be assessed simply. It can't be done just by comparing the cost of a bed at St Thomas' with the relatively modest cost of a bed at the Centre for the duration of a patient's stay. To get a full picture, costs should be offset in a variety of ways beyond my skill against a range of hypothetical alternatives for each patient. But no such mercenary judgement of the Centre's work should fail at least to take into account the relief care that makes all the difference for people like Mrs Q between being able to stay in their own home and having to go into some kind of long-term care — Part III accommodation or a geriatric ward, neither of which is an attractive proposition for someone who still has a modicum of independence or an almost sufficiency of care at home.

Many carers are themselves elderly, like Mrs Q's brother, and cannot manage any longer without some help. Or the carer him or herself may be not so well and in need of a break in order to regather their strength. A GP tells of one of her patients, Mrs R, who was 81 years old and rather confused. She was in the general hospital where stomach cancer had been diagnosed. There was nothing further they could do for her and the bed was needed. But the GP knew that the daughter who looked after Mrs R was herself suffering from heart disease and at that moment not well enough to receive her mother home. So the GP arranged for Mrs R to be transferred from the general hospital to the Centre where her family could visit her informally and often and she was 'successfully mobilised and discharged home after her daughter had had a good break'.

Sometimes, where there is just one carer, probably a single daughter looking after a parent, the situation becomes more than physically burdensome for the carer. Fear and dependence in the person being looked after breed more fear and dependence until the patient becomes very demanding, unable to let their main support out of their sight. The person doing the caring can then easily become more and more exhausted and resentful. There's something about the smallness, warmth and informality of the Centre that has made it possible for a few people who had previously 'refused' (by all sorts of means) to let their carer have a holiday to accept a temporary separation. 'Lip service is paid to the enormous work done by carers in the community of disabled relatives', wrote one GP indignantly on their behalf.

> Mr S, an elderly gentleman with asthma and anxiety and over-dependence on his daughter, was admitted to the Centre for a review allowing his daughter to have two weeks' holiday. On previous occasions when the daughter tried to go on holiday the patient would suffer a 'relapse' and the holiday would have to be terminated. In this case both the father and the daughter benefited and she is now able to resume the onerous care of her father.

The child who stays with a parent in order to look after that parent is as needy and deserving of support as the elderly spouse or sibling who acts as a carer. It is precisely such 'children' who, because of what they have given up in order to go on caring, sometimes within a suffocatingly demanding relationship, are likely to end up without anyone to care for them should they become ill.

Some carers are also working to support the family financially and become very stretched between their work and the needs of their dependent relative. Mrs T, for example, a widow, works full-time and while she is at work her son, 'handicapped by spina bifida with hydrocephalus and epilepsy', goes to a day centre. Since her son needs her to help him to go to the lavatory several times a night, Mrs T gets very tired. She wants to care for her son herself as much as she can but has nevertheless found that the occasional break is worthwhile in terms of recouping energies. 'She feels guilty at not being able to cope alone but realises she is exhausted and her son needs respite care. She knows that she has support at the Centre that she can call upon.'

It's this personal knowledge of the Centre that allows tired people to trust their relatives to it for a while. Staff always visit and meet both carer and cared-for before the first admission so that the patient is greeted by someone familiar on arrival at Centre. There are people who would never have taken a break if it had meant entrusting their charge to a distant, large and frequently unattractive institution (and anyway opportunities for short stay in such institutions are now diminishing). Among them were the parents of U, a woman in her thirties with severe mental and physical handicaps. They had never been parted from her before, ever, but 'for the first time in her life they had found a place staffed by the kind of people they trust to care for her while they visit family abroad' (her GP talking).

The Centre copes equally well with this kind of planned respite admission and with emergency admissions when, for some reason — often because the carer is taken ill, the situation at home breaks down. This latter kind of admission is all the easier for the patient if, as often happens, they know the Centre already, have begun to look on it as a safe temporary refuge. In the case of Mrs E, already mentioned in chapter 3, staff knew her well enough from previous visits to spot and relieve her anxieties about the reasons for her admission, about the degree of her husband's ill health.

One GP, reflecting on the value of the Centre within the West Lambeth Health Authority, identified as one of the six useful extra services offered by the Centre.

> An important facility providing care for patients while their carers have a break or, in some cases, receive hospital care. This facility is available at short notice where the carer needs urgent care themselves and is provided in the community, thus causing minimum disruption to the patient. Four of my patients have benefited from this service in the last 12 months, two of them at very short notice.

(His other five factors are the possibilities of 'communication and education for those working in primary health care in this District', the 'important facility for the treatment of acute breakdowns in the elderly', the terminal care, the accessible physio and OT and the rehabilitation of patients who have received treatment in the DGH.)

Another GP is so convinced of the value of the Centre's respite care work that he says it could be renamed the Community Carers' Centre. It's obvious that many people working in primary health care and seeing at first-hand what some families cope with feel very strongly about this need to care for carers. Without underestimating the valuable support offered by the community services, I have to say that the Centre, precisely because it is a place, a safe place, offers something extra. It offers the security of knowing that a pleasant haven not far from home is available as and when necessary and it also offers a continuing personal relationship. Not only do staff visit the patients' homes but carers are encouraged to call in at the Centre between admissions, to discuss their problems or just to chat.

One of the sisters describes a patient, Mrs V, who was first admitted with shingles but also very depressed because both her sister and the person who'd lived next door for decades had just died. As her health became worse she had several further admissions to the Centre becoming frailer all the time. She finally came in for what looked like a last visit with urinary problems but asked if, with family help, she could go home again.

> We had built up a good relationship with the family and when the going got tough they called round for practical and emotional support. We lent them draw-sheets, bed-pan etc, so they could nurse her at home. During the difficult time at the end the daughter called in to see us for support and reassurance. This situation worked well as the family had established a firm relationship with the staff over a long period of time and felt welcome to call in unannounced for help. The management of Mrs V was a team effort, GP, district nurse and us.

Not just a rest

Care for carers doesn't, however, supersede care for patients themselves. In no way are patients who come in for respite care seen merely as burden of which carers are temporarily relieved. Quite the opposite. As the GP whose patient used to set up his easel in the conservatory said, 'The ease with which severely disabled patients can be accommodated and the pleasure they give to the CCC and receive from these admissions is one of the features of the work of the Centre.'

With their emphasis on patient autonomy, staff naturally use the time of such an admission to see how they can help the patient towards greater independence or control. For someone who has been too much within one very narrow setting, the Centre offers the opportunity to expand into increased sociability. For the mentally handicapped woman who had never left her own home before there was a new knowledge that she could exist in a different environment and make her own relationships. For other people, perhaps particularly elderly people who have become accustomed to dependence, there is help available with mobility, even if it's just relearning the confidence to take a few steps away from the chair where they have been wont to sit all day. Or it may be that the Centre can help with advice about bladder control or ways of coping with incontinence to make it less of an embarrassment and a burden.

The Centre is particularly well-equipped by its general

approach to help those patients who have become unnecessarily passive. A paraplegic patient, for instance, who was admitted for a week to give his wife a break, 'was frightened of becoming more independent, e.g. in catheter care, and had difficulty in coming to terms with the fact that he was expected to say when he would like to do things, e.g. when he would like to get up, whether he would have a wash or a bath'.

Not that baths aren't encouraged. One very simple matter in which patients admitted for respite care can often be stimulated to do more for themselves is in the area of personal hygiene. They may have come to look on washing as onerous and difficult and to have got in the way of leaving it all to someone else. Without being too bossy about it, Centre staff employ friendly and often effective persuasion in this direction.

> A patient admitted whilst her daughter was on holiday had leg ulcers and a catheter. Part of the aim of the admission was to improve her self-care (hygiene, diet), to look after her catheter care, to see if her leg ulcers could be improved and to see if her sleeping pattern could be improved (she slept in a chair at home because her bed was too small). By the time she was discharged, she was taking more care of herself — she asked to be washed and also washed her top half herself; special bandages resulted in an improvement to her ulcers and a change in her night sedation meant that she slept better.

A respite admission then is seen as an opportunity to assess the patient's physical and mental functioning, to offer any available medical aid and to enlist the patient in an attempt at greater independence. Sometimes, of course, the best efforts of staff may come up against stronger factors elsewhere. There was one elderly gentleman who found while in the Centre that he could, very slowly, get about on his own again. But as soon as he arrived home he was popped straight back into bed by his wife who actually preferred not to have him up and about under her feet.

There are always going to be occasions when Centre staff, however hard they try, cannot actually change a situation. It would be doing the work there no service to portray it as inevitably effective.

Mrs W, a woman in her seventies, living with her daughter

who was herself unwell, was referred to the Centre for a week so that her mobility could be assessed, her continence improved and social support systems set up for her return home. She went home, after what staff candidly describe as a very trying week,with a new bed, full social service back-up and attendance at the day unit fixed up, but with very little desire to try to help herself. When Mrs W's daughter broke her ankle and Mrs W had to be re-admitted they found that, for all the offers of support, both Mrs W's health and her home circumstances had deteriorated. She had bed sores which didn't clear in the Centre and soon after she returned home again had to be taken into a long-stay ward where, shortly afterwards, she died.

By and large, though, the perception by patient and carer that it's safe to take a break (together with the patient's experience of having been focused on and stimulated) relaxes a home situation which may have been getting tense.

Managing on your own

Some of the patients who come in for respite care have no one to look after them; they are people whose health just allows them to cope alone with an effort. For them regular admission may be what makes it possible for them to carry on, may pre-empt the prospect of increasing numbers of emergency admissions followed by a move into permanent institutional care.

Mrs X is a delightful, independent 95-year-old lady with congestive heart failure who manages well at home but from time to time her chest problems flare up. She becomes depressed and generally unwell. She was admitted to us on several occasions and took two–three weeks to overcome her poorly physical and emotional problems. After much discussion with her, her son, a GP and us at the Centre, it was decided to bring her in every six weeks for one week, active prophylactic management rather than lurch from crisis to crisis. She has responded well to this and in the last six months has remained fairly stable. This has enabled her to stay in her own home as independently as possible. She may well from time to time have ended up in an acute bed with her chest problems.

As Miss A said, the knowledge that there is somewhere you are cared for, somewhere you can turn to, helps you to keep going. You aren't just discharged to struggle on alone. You know that if life gets too much you'll be able to go back for 'respite'.

There are other ways, too, in which the Centre offers relief from burdens. Once in a while it may be the GP to whom they are offering respite. It can happen that a patient becomes so pressing with his or her demands that this takes up time which can ill be afforded from other patients and creates an undue strain on the GP. A patient with such a need for reassurance that he or she rings the GP every day and most nights as well as can be 'weaned' on to the Centre, finding enough support there to ease up on the GP. Not that there is any sentimentality at the Centre about being open and available beyond what staff can bear.

Mr Y was so lonely and anxious that he had been in touch with his GP every single day about some ailment or other and was beginning to cause considerable strain and irritation. When he was given the chance to come to the day unit on certain regular days, he ceased to demand so much attention from the GP's surgery. But since, given half a chance, he would have translated his hunger for attention into turning up at the Centre morning, noon and night, he was given certain ground rules — brief social visits to the day unit on days other than 'his' days were allowed but only on condition that they *were* social visits and he did not (as was his custom) talk at length about his various ailments and complaints. He could do that when he was there officially as a patient. While this arrangement worked well in terms of taking pressure off the GP, it still needed constant vigilance by Centre staff to prevent Mr Y becoming a nuisance to other patients or too much of a pressure on staff themselves. It is typical, however, that the administrator, who had been as involved as anyone in Mr Y's regime, said that their main anxiety was that they had been unable to find the key that would 'unlock' Mr Y's misery, allow him to come out of the prison built of endless boring demands which simply alienated potential friends and acquaintances. It was something still to be pondered over and hoped for.

9 Dying

People die the way they want to here.

(Senior nurse)

From the frequency with which death has already been mentioned, it'll be clear that it's an integral part of life at the Centre — and I mean 'life'; that's not a bad joke. Death here is a central experience, not just an unseemly failure to 'cure'. It's a natural and inevitable part of life. And one of the Centre's roles is to be a place where people can die with knowledge and with dignity.

The big general hospital, geared to treatment and to care, is often a bad place to die in, a bad place to have to wait for death. And at home, for all the good work of the St Thomas' Terminal Care Support Team, there may come a time when relatives can't manage or the person living alone can't cope. Hospices have done a great job not just in the care they offer but in pioneering and disseminating a new concern with the process of dying. However, the nearest hospice is some way away and, too, there are positive arguments for looking after dying people in the midst of life.

One GP, looking back over the Centre's terminal-care work during its first year, felt a retrospective regret for a patient of his who died before the Centre came into being.

> If only the Community Care Centre had been available for
> Z who died in the hospice of a brain tumour after three or
> four months. The care at the hospice was, of course, very
> good, but Z's wife complained about the expense and
> difficulty of travelling to and from the hospice which

involved long waits for two different buses. If he had been in the CCC his wife and two young daughters could have visited him more easily. As the family doctor I had looked after Z's parents and have had the pleasure of seeing his wife and daughters recover from the traumatic final year of his slow-growing brain tumour. After knowing Z for 20 years, not being responsible for his care during his final illness probably mattered to him and his family and it certainly mattered to me.

Truth-telling

It has been an integral part of the Centre's policy from the beginning to be honest with patients. Truth-telling isn't, of course, a crass matter of 'here's all the worst information, like it or not'. It's more a matter of never lying to a patient, always answering queries as fully as possible and providing an atmosphere in which people can easily and unselfconsciously ask their questions.

It's clear to Centre staff from their experience that most people want to know what's happening to them, to be able to feel to some extent still in control of their lives — and deaths. An honest response to this desire need not mean using the word 'death' in every other sentence. A moment of realisation and/or acceptance can occur in a simple conversation about the likelihood of going home again. On the other hand, a great many patients and families are only too glad of the opportunity to talk about death directly. This can be part of the process of enabling the patient to die with some degree of self-possession and the family and friends to be free of regrets about the manner of death.

Occasionally there are difficulties caused by conflicting attitudes. Then Centre staff would put the patient's needs above all. Miss BA, for example. Though capable of living alone, as she did, Miss BA was of less than average intelligence and had always been protected by her siblings. The fact that Miss BA had cancer was known to her family but had been kept from her. In the Centre, however, where Miss BA was admitted several times for the relief of symptoms, honest answers were given to her questions. Miss BA's siblings were angry about this but Miss BA, whose initial response was anger of a different kind — with the illness and the lack of a cure for it, was then able to make choices about the last weeks, to live these positively. 'It was felt that Miss BA's admission to the Centre allowed her to "grow up" and gain some independence . . . it had freed her to live some life for a short period. It was felt that the Centre had been the patient's asylum.'

Before her admission to the Centre, Miss BA's doctor, working alone in a situation where he had been frequently and forcibly reminded of her brothers' and sisters' desire that Miss BA be kept in ignorance, had not felt able to tell her the truth. In the Centre it was easier; it was a setting in which Miss BA could be her own person. The GP was glad of this truth-telling and its results, while having to take quite a lot of the family's anger about it.

Not all GPs are wholly comfortable with this policy of honesty, but it's seen as absolutely essential by Centre staff, integral to the idea of the patient as an equal partner in health care. A GP who can't cope with this will by and large tend not to use the Centre for terminal care. Those who do are as enthusiastic as the staff about treating their patients with the respect which demands honesty.

All in it together

A 70-year-old patient, who had first been admitted to a geriatric ward elsewhere because her main symptom was extreme confusion, collapsed and was taken to St Thomas' for investigation. A scan revealed gross cerebral secondaries. Treated with steroids, she became less confused. She was then referred to the Centre for terminal care. Communication is said to have been very good all round in this case and it was in discussion between the patient and her family and the GP and Centre staff and the terminal care support team that the decision was made to discontinue treatment. 'The aim of the referral was to allow the patient to die with dignity and peace.'

The same GP who regretted that the Centre hadn't been there for Z also used the word 'dignity' in describing the crucial last days of another patient with a brain tumour.

> Tact, tolerance and caring ability of the CCC staff the best
> Mrs CB could have obtained. Her daughter appreciated

everything done for her. GP/terminal care support team worked closely with the CCC nurses and several medical students observed and discussed this difficult area of medical care personified by Mrs CB whose dignity was maintained in spite of incontinence and occasional aggressive verbal outbursts.

The whole health-care team at the Centre, with valuable backing from the terminal care support team, is involved in the care of dying patients. Therapists who are more accustomed to getting people going again than to helping them to die have been able to use their skills in terminal care, too. An OT may be able to help with something as simple as showing a patient with failing strength an easier way to hold a cup. A physio may be able, by manipulation or demonstration of the best way to lie, to ease someone's breathing. The dietician may suggest appropriate nourishment for someone who can eat very little. A secretary may spare some time each day for a chat. And, of course, nurses and GP play primary roles, with the continuity of care by the family doctor being especially valuable to dying patients and their families.

However, all the team effort doesn't go into producing a certain pre-conceived pattern of what death should be like. The team tries to direct its energies into attentive awareness of the patient in order to assist that patient to die as they would wish. Not everyone is going to want to go gently into that good night. Some will need to rage against the dying of the light, which is harder for bystanders to bear than acceptance. Some — like the patient with cerebral secondaries — may even have their personalities altered by the illness. It is always a temptation to desire for a dying patient an acceptance of death, perhaps even to attempt to induce such acceptance prematurely. But then, from all accounts, it seems to be a rare person who — given the necessary information — does not in the end wish to die with their own kind of dignity.

Certainly, the staff are now quite convinced that people choose — however inarticulately — the timing of their death. Often this takes the form of letting go sooner than the GP or consultant had predicted. Examples were already to be found within the first few weeks of the Centre's life. One man, admitted to die but expected to take about a week or so, died after one day in the Centre. 'It seemed that the patient relaxed when he was admitted and decided that he would die.' Another patient, who came in to give his wife a rest on what was seen as his long, slow progress towards death, 'died on the Sunday before his planned discharge the following Wednesday'. In his case, again, it seemed that he had relaxed into the Centre and chose not to make the further effort of going home — 'he liked being in the CCC, he thought it was a nice place to be, he could see the trees, it was peaceful and people cared. He like sitting in the greenhouse which he described as "outside".'

More recently a clergyman patient pre-empted the projected time of his dying but, looking back afterwards, staff could see that he died when he'd done all the last things that he had set himself — he had gone to a particular wedding and taken part in a service arranged within the Centre (the Centre's greater closeness to home than to hospital is reflected in the fact that it has no chaplaincy; local clergy continue to minister to members of their congregations).

The dying person will always know better than anyone else can their own rhythm, their own pace, but, as the nurses become more attuned to dying patients, they can sometimes recognise the approach of death even when there are no clear medical indicators. When Mrs E, who was mentioned earlier, came in for a period of respite care which looked to all appearances just like her previous admissions, it was her special nurse who said, no, this time Mrs E has come in to die — and she did.

The facts of death

The story of Mrs E has a lighter sequel which nevertheless says something about attitudes to dying within the Centre. Before she died Mrs E had had a bath and had her hair washed. It so happened that later, after she had died and was by common consent still lying in her own bed, a volunteer manicurist was working in the Centre. A fellow-patient decided that it would be nice for Mrs E to have her nails done and asked the manicurist if she'd just pop in to their bedroom to give Mrs E a manicure. Finding the room and seeing curtains round the bed, the manicurist asked if there were anything wrong. 'Well', said another patient in the room judiciously, 'she is dead.' The manicurist, no one having thought to mention this to her previously, departed in a panic and, accosting the nearest nurse, demanded to know if she were aware she had a corpse on her hands. Being busy, the nurse replied casually that of course she knew, there was nothing unusual about letting dead people stay in their beds for up to 24 hours. This did nothing to diminish the manicurist's consternation but it does illustrate a gloriously accepting attitude to the facts of death, an attitude which has permeated pretty quickly through staff and patients, many of the latter themselves old and ailing.

In a big hospital there's little chance of coming to terms with the simple fact of the body of the dead person. In the Centre, in the administrator's words, dying is 'completely natural and informal. The patient dies and it is like dying at home — no shrouds, no fridges and no mad rush to hide the body.' Some necessary paperwork may have to be done with relatives but it will be done by people who know all about the patient and have probably met the family before. The undertakers eventually come for the body, as from home, with the GP providing the death certificate.

Mr DC was 81 and had congestive cardiac failure. He'd been into the Centre before and, on his last admission, when clearly failing.

> He was able to talk about it — with his family — and was prepared for death when it came. Mr DC died at midnight; his son stayed till morning, talking to the night nurses, popping in to see his dad and — he said — being able to come to terms with the fact that his father had died. Mr DC had a reputation in the community as the 'kind gentleman'. He was taken out by the undertakers with his hat on and waved goodbye by friends in the day unit.

The relatives, or anyone who minds about the dying person come to that, are also felt to be a part of the Centre's work, part of the Centre. There's an atmosphere which encourages people to talk about how they really feel even if that differs from a conventional expectation of how they ought to feel. In one instance, a woman was able to express pent-up negative feelings about her husband. After that she could be with him while he died in a way she had begun to fear would be impossible.

And after death the caring continues. No one is hustled away; relatives and friends can stay with the body as long as they feel they need to and the staff's close involvement doesn't end with the patient's death. In the case of the patient mentioned earlier who died unexpectedly after one day in the Centre,

> the ward sister had carried out a home visit before admission and she also attended his funeral. Two nurses visited his wife early in the morning to tell her that her husband had died. They had a cup of tea with her and waited for both her and a neighbour to get dressed before going back to the CCC with them to see her husband.

Staff often go to the funerals of patients whom they have come to care about.

For some relatives the Centre continues to be important after their experience with death there. A GP describes the relationship of one couple with the Centre:

> Mrs ED is a 75-year-old lady whose husband was admitted to the CCC in the first few weeks of its opening. He was in his eighties and had a carcinoma of the prostate. The couple lived locally in the house where Mrs ED was born. Mr ED was admitted originally to give his wife a break but, as he became increasingly weak in the terminal stages of his illness, he was finally admitted and died in the CCC. Mrs Ed gained a lot of support from all the staff at the CCC and was pleased that he had not needed to be admitted to hospital and had had continuity of care throughout. The CCC became an important part of her life — she was involved with cooking for the cake stall and when, after an operation, she herself needed extra attention, she was admitted for convalescence for a short while.

A part of her life, not just somewhere for treating illnesses or even for sheltered death. And this is because staff at the Centre, in taking patients and their relatives seriously, are offering a human relationship which isn't just paternal/maternal but at least in part mutual and open to learning on the staff side.

Always learning

In the terminal care work, there's been a lot of learning, some from the people who've died and some from their relatives. After one death early on, before the present degree of natural openness had been established, staff were still earnestly debating whether and how they should tell the other patients while the family were already discussing all the details with these other patients 'over tea in the greenhouse'.

But for all the now-established attitude of openness and sharing, terminal care remains very demanding of staff, particularly when they do not defend themselves against becoming involved. It's not always easy to know whose pain you are coping with. As the senior nurse said, if you know that a dying patient is going to choke and turn blue if they try to drink and yet at that moment they want a sip of milk more than anything, are you reluctant to give it because of the discomfort they'll suffer or the discomfort that you'll suffer, watching? In this case, the practical Centre answer was, having already made sure that the patient was well-informed about the effects of her illness, to accept her wishes as paramount and provide the milk.

That example comes from one patient's story which may be worth telling in more detail because it includes many aspects of the Centre's terminal care work. Mrs FE was the Centre's first patient with motor neurone disease. Hospices are accustomed to the nursing of it but it's not common enough, this slow death of the body's motor nerves, even for all GPs to have come across it.

When Mrs FE was admitted to the Centre at the beginning of December, it was thought that she might have as much as a year to live and the plan was to make her life as comfortable as possible, to help her with swallowing, with communication (speech had gone) and with breathing (more and more of an effort). There was talk at this stage of where Mrs FE would go when she left: could she go home and go on going to her day centre? The nurses tended her and observed the effects of her illness, noting particularly how her nights were disturbed by waking with breathlessness or panicky choking because of her lack of a cough reflex. On any occasion when she had had a good night's sleep this was remarked on with pleasure.

The dietician specified a liquid diet and the precise recording of just what food Mrs FE was able to take. The speech therapist suggested which position of the head would make swallowing easiest and was involved in getting a keyboard communicator for Mrs FE to see if it would work better than handwriting. The OT assessed Mrs FE's mobility and recommended a particular kind of wheelchair as well as finding out that she'd like to go to social events in the day unit downstairs. The physios concerned themselves with Mrs FE's breathing and which angle of the bed, which position for Mrs FE would make it easiest.

Whenever the nurses became bothered by a particular symptom and felt that they weren't relieving it as best they could, the GP called and within a month there had been several meetings of GP, therapists and nurses to discuss what best to do next. Mrs FE was able to go to one or two social occasions downstairs and to visit her family for Christmas Day. After Christmas she became increasingly upset by her breathing difficulties and her inability to cough or spit to get rid of choking phlegm. A lot of effort was put into finding ways of relieving these symptoms, including the use of suction, but it was Mrs FE's fear and agitation that needed relief as much as anything so her GP suggested tranquillising medication. Because Mrs FE could communicate only briefly in writing, it is possible even now to recall whole conversations with her. The nurse said to her: 'Do you feel it difficult to breathe?'

Mrs FE: Yes.

Nurse: Do you want to talk about it?

Mrs FE: Yes.

Nurse: Are you aware that we cannot improve it — only help to take away the fear?

Mrs FE: Yes. It is terrible.

Nurse: We will give you some medication to help you.

Mrs FE: Yes. Thanks.

It began to seem that predictions of Mrs FE's ever going home again had been over-optimistic. Mrs FE's family talked with both GP and Centre staff who were concerned that they should be fully in the picture. On the first Friday in January, when Mrs FE's condition was worsening, her family spent a long time in the Centre and talked a lot with staff about death, death in general and deaths in the family. With Mrs FE they were natural and chatty, bringing her family news, etc.

On the Saturday feeding by tube was started and provision

made for further sedation as necessary. With suction to clear her lungs, Mrs FE managed to sleep for some of Saturday night. On Sunday morning she complained that the pain in her legs was now terrible (crampy pains had been coming on for a while), so bad that it troubled her even more than the breathlessness. She was given a warm bath and, later, after phone consultation with the GP, a syringe driver was set up to give her a steady dosage of diamorphine.

At some point during the previous few days Mrs FE had written 'I want to go home' and had gently been told that she would never go home again, to which she replied, 'Oh all right . . . I like it here.' On the Sunday afternoon, when her family were with her, Mrs FE wrote, 'I am scared' but, as the diamorphine took care of the pain and she relaxed, she wrote 'OK' and, later, her last word, 'fine'. By early evening she had become calm and peaceful and in mid-evening, with her family round her, quietly died. Later her grandchildren came in to say goodbye to her.

This story shows some of the positive features of the Centre's terminal care — the caring, the team work, the openness with patient and relatives, the constant sensitivity to new needs. But it didn't all come easily. The nurses were very troubled by Mrs FE's distress at times and by not being able to provide instant relief. Even after Mrs FE had died, while acknowledging that her last few hours 'were beautiful', they were anxiously looking back over everything that had happened, admitting to anger with the illness, with themselves, with one another. The senior nurse was cross with herself for not realising sooner that death was approaching as fast as it was and admitted that she'd then felt out of step with the GP and annoyed with him that he seemed even slower to recognise how near death was. Would Mrs FE's last couple of days have been even better if the morphine driver had been brought into action earlier? All this is gone over partly because staff need an outlet for their own feelings and partly in order to learn for the next time.

Not all suffering can always be relieved. The real regard for patients that makes the Centre's terminal care so vital means that staff will themselves sometimes be hurt. But to an outside eye it seems that Mrs FE, like so many of the Centre's patients, had all the support needed to 'make a good death'.

10 OK to be Old

Probably, if I was to single out a specific and isolated virtue of the CCC, I would have to say that there have been cases late at night of old people living alone who, by virtue of relatively trivial disease, necessitate immediate nursing . . . looking at my list of patients, I can see five such cases which were admitted in the evening and I was able to see my patient within one hour of my examination, now in a warm bed surrounded with all the panoply of an ultra-modern nursing unit.

(A GP)

Devoting a separate chapter to praising the way in which the Centre does *not* ghetto-ise the elderly may appear somewhat perverse. However, the needs of older people are of pressing concern in a society with ever-increasing numbers of older people. It is against this background that it's worth looking specifically at the value of a small general medical centre in relation to old, increasingly frail people.

The Centre does not replace any of the existing services for the elderly. It does not reproduce the high-tech medicine of the hospital; it does not offer long-term care of the kind to be found in specialised geriatric units; it most certainly does not supersede any of the community services which are already working flat out to maintain people in their own homes.

Appropriate care
What it does furnish is a new facility particularly suitable for elderly patients — or rather two intertwined facilities: one, the

rehabilitative day unit which helps physically infirm people with shaken confidence or lowered morale to look after themselves again; and two, in-patient nursing care for older people too ill to remain at home alone or with equally elderly relatives. These are the very circumstances in which older people can begin to feel exposed and out of control. They may be whisked, of necessity, into a bed in a general hospital which they don't really need medically speaking; they may suspect that, if they can't manage on their own at home when they get ill, then someone somewhere is going to start muttering about old people's homes.

The Centre makes available just the level of care needed — oversight from the familiar GP and sympathetic nursing — while relating that care to what the patient wants for his or her own future. More often than not what the patient wants is to return home and, once a patient is in touch with the Centre, that return home can be made in the security of knowing there is a local place of asylum (in its best and original sense).

One GP, with long experience of the area, spoke of the Centre's 'important facility for the treatment of acute break-downs in the elderly which do not need high-technology medical care. The medical supervision of these patients is free of charge to the District, as are also the drugs provided. Rehabilitation and length of stay in hospital facilities are reduced to a minimum.'

Some of the Centre's older patients are very old indeed. One GP describes

> the oldest patient on our lists [who], at 105 years, suffers from recurrent chest infections, secondary to bronchiecta-sis. Chest infections always respond to intensive phy-siotherapy, antibiotics and steroids. Two admissions to the Centre when her chest became worse were both very successful and probably very appropriate, as she is a friendly, sociable lady.

We've already seen how a patient of a mere 95 was supported in her own home by regular admissions to the Centre. In both these cases, a bed in a general hospital was not necessary but nor could the patient manage at home at times. The small, friendly Centre with its after-care provisions and community links is the ideal mid-way kind of care.

In the Centre you are a patient like any other; you are not labelled 'old' since both ward and day unit are open to all sorts and conditions of local people over the age of 16. Nevertheless, there is an acknowledgement within the Centre that, placed as it is in a stable, rather ageing community, it may have a special role in relation to older people.

In February 1986 a consultant physician with a particular interest in the needs of the elderly came to talk to an audit meeting about just this subject. Conversation ranged over Centre admissions and referral to consultants, the best approach to assessment of the general health of elderly patients and the role of the day unit in the rehabilitation of older people.

Many of the patients discussed in earlier chapters are over 70, which goes to show that the age of a patient is seldom the most important thing about them. However, there's no denying that being old can bring problems in its train beyond just illness or even the fear or insecurity engendered by that illness. Some suffer from a general increased frailty which means that the questions asked must be different from those that would apply to a younger patient. When a woman of 84 was referred to the day unit with increasing pain from her rheumatoid arthritis and it was found that she had an acutely painful left hip, a 2-inch shortening of her left femur and the distinct possibility of a pathological fracture of the hip, the big question was — what should be done about it given that the patient had already been very much weakened by a five-month stay in hospital the previous year? At the stage when this problem was debated at audit meeting no conclusion had been reached other than that, after the X-ray (if it confirmed the suspicion), GP and Centre staff should consult with an orthopaedic specialist about what best to do.

Being old and ill can also bring with it problems of either isolation or unwelcome increased dependence, as Mrs GF's GP points out.

> Mrs GF was a lady in her mid-seventies whose husband died of a mesothelioma [cancer of the pleura] three years ago. Shortly thereafter she herself was found to have a carcinoma of the bronchus. She was an independent person who coped well with her radiotherapy. However, she

gradually found it more difficult to manage at home and spent increasing time with her son's family. This involved using a grand-daughter's bed, which upset Mrs GF. She was admitted to the Centre in the spring for a few weeks. During this time, despite her breathlessness, she became more confident and mobile, was able to return to her flat where she lived on her own. Regaining her independence was very important to the whole family.

A similar use of the Centre was made by the same GP for another patient of 88 who lived alone until she had to have a cholecystectomy (gall bladder removal) and was in hospital for 3½ months. Afterwards, her family found it difficult to cope with supporting her at home; she was admitted to the Centre, learnt to walk again with a frame and became mobile and active enough to return home while arrangements were made for more long-term care elsewhere.

With the best will in the world and the best support that the Centre can offer, it does still sometimes become necessary for an old person to give up living alone. Where the Centre cannot stave off loss of total independence, it can sometimes offer a transitional haven, a place where an older patient can reconsider the way they've been living, contemplate future options realistically and reach their own decision.

An old man living alone [who] has airways disease . . . just copes with help from social services and neighbours. He developed an acute exacerbation of his chest problems and became bed-bound. In the CCC he is cared for by myself as his GP and nursing staff geared to maintaining the patient's independence. He has immediate access to physiotherapy and occupational therapy assessment. In this 'safe' environment *he* begins to accept that he will not be able to continue living on his own. Social services are involved and discharge to Part III is arranged after five weeks.

Where an older patient doesn't live alone, the people who support them may also be elderly or ailing. This was so for Mrs HG whose story also shows how a physical symptom which is not serious in itself may become more painful or alarming when associated with already existing handicaps.

Mrs HG complained of abdominal pain. Her blind male neighbour, chief carer, requested visit. After the bad night she had had and because of limitation of home care and doubt about cause of abdominal pain, admission essential. Having decided not surgical, GP took opportunity of using CCC to try to make diagnosis and relieve symptoms. Faecal impaction (even if rectal examination done in patient's home), the delay in nurses arriving and the discomfort of the necessary enema and subsequent evacuation for a woman crippled with osteo-arthritis in hips and knees could well have prolonged doubt about getting better and physical suffering. During the week of Mrs HG's stay in the Centre it was noted how devoted the blind friend was to her. Unfortunately he died soon after the incident.

Physical frailty in older people may be accompanied by some confusion — or, indeed, the confusion many come without physical frailty. For some serve conditions, where there is little remedial treatment available, some kind of long-term care may be the only answer. But there are all sorts and degrees of confusion and many are susceptible of treatment, help, amelioration.

A widow in her seventies, living alone with family close by, had a CVA (stroke) which left her with marked memory loss and confusion. Although physically well, she could not manage alone at home and was a risk with cooking, heating, etc. She attended the day unit for OT regularly and made excellent progress and led an increasingly independent life with occasional support from her family. The OT staff were able to carry out regular assessments in her home, thus completing the link between community and hospital services. Unexpectedly, while in the day unit she suffered a grand mal epileptic fit. I was able to visit her within the Centre and found her confused and distressed. Admission to an in-patient bed was arranged immediately. Here she remained looked after by staff and a GP whom she knew well already. Urgent neurological assessment was arranged on an out-patient basis without the need for hospital admission. She has made a good recovery and is now discharged but still seen by the OT for monthly review.

The familiarity of the staff, of the GP, of the neighbourhood — all have been commented on as helping to reassure nervous older patients who have lived all their lives in North Lambeth or North Southwark. They may dread compulsory removal from what is familiar and find the Centre comfortingly embedded in the neighbourhood. True, St Thomas' is also in North Lambeth, only a short walk away, but go down to the Embankment and into the large, efficient hospital and you could be anywhere. As one patient remarked of the old Lambeth Hospital, to go to St Thomas' you feel the need to change into your best clothes but you could pop round to the Lambeth in your pinny. And the same is most certainly true of the Centre, if not more so.

At the Centre, patients are free to go out, if well enough, for a coffee or a curry or a pint or to visit relatives in nearby streets, just as relatives can drop in at any time. Indeed, such coming and going may be promulgated as part of the treatment plan. And even within the Centre, the low windows with window seats allow patients to watch the comings and goings in Monkton Street as they might from their own front rooms. We heard earlier how, after a stroke, one patient learnt to get about again in the familiar local streets. Another patient, an in-patient, 'severely disorientated by a major stroke made a sudden decisive improvement when he went out in a wheelchair and discovered he was on his own home territory.'

The closeness to home of the Centre — both in its literal physical sense and in the way that staff see the place as more like home than like hospital — is particularly valuable then for older patients. So is the multi-disciplinary nature of the Centre's work. Illnesses which tend to afflict the elderly — chest problems, arthritis, ulcers — respond not just to medication (or not at all to medication) but also to physiotherapy, occupational therapy, nursing care and diet. A patient like Mr IH who has rheumatoid arthritis and can just about walk with a frame, who is hard of hearing, incontinent and bothered by a painful shoulder, who lives alone and scrapes by with visits from neighbours and the support of his home help — a patient like that can be brought by ambulance into the day unit where he can be seen by nurses, physiotherapists, OTs, the chiropodist and his GP relatively informally and easily all in one place. Mr IH, as it happens, finds

103

the strain of coping alone too much, positively wants to move into a home, but to get into Part III accommodation you have to be continent and so far none of the methods tried has worked. So what's to do? At the day-unit staff meeting which discussed this all ways round no answer was reached.

However, if any therapist or nurse had had an answer it would have been found since all problems are discussed and all members of the team have their contributions to make. It's often useful for an older patient to talk to a dietician, patients who've had strokes can find the speech therapy at the Centre a boon and very many of the older patients appreciate the opportunity to see the chiropodist while they're there. All these services are openly available. There's no need to get a new GP referral for a new kind of therapist as there might be if they were all in different places. And it's possible for people from the neighbourhood to refer themselves for speech therapy or chiropody.

In the dentist's chair

Maybe slightly less obvious than the fact that foot problems can get worse with age is the fact that many elderly people have both teeth problems and a deep-rooted fear of going to the dentist, often resulting from experience of dentistry years ago before effective pain-killing measures were on offer. The Centre's dentist says that he has heard innumerable horror stories of such experiences as having all your teeth our without anaesthetic.

Through his screening programme, the dentist has picked up lots of tooth decay, neglect and pain in older patients and has been able to persuade them to accept treatment, Mrs JI is typical.

> Initial conversations with this lady took place in the doorway of the dental surgery because Mrs JI was too frightened to come and sit on the dental chair . . . After talking to her for some time and having explained that no treatment would be provided unless she agreed to it, she consented to return the following week.
>
> During the second visit, Mrs JI came into the surgery and actually sat down on the dental chair. I explained that the purpose of the visit was for me to ask her some general and dental health questions followed by a dental examination.
>
> Mrs JI agreed to this as long as I promised not to do any

fillings! I acquiesced to this after reiterating the purpose of the visit. Mrs JI was nervous; apart from rapid breathing, perspiration could be seen on her forehead. She did, however, allow the dental examination to be completed.

Inspection of the oral cavity revealed that Mrs JI had neglected caring for her mouth and a considerable amount of treatment was necessary to make her dentally fit. I informed Mrs JI that it would be possible to carry out all her treatment at the LCCC while she was attending the day unit. At this point she repeated her fears of receiving dental treatment. I was able to reassure her that there would be no pain involved and that, if at any time during the treatment she wished to terminate it, she could do so. At the end of the session we agreed that at the next visit some treatment would be carried out on the side that was causing her discomfort.

The third visit saw the initiation of active dental treatment. This consisted of the surgical removal of buried/broken roots. Although this may not sound very pleasant, Mrs JI in fact expressed surprise at the end of the appointment because she did not feel any pain and secondly it was over before she had time to worry.

Mrs JI continued to attend for many more dental visits. Apart from some more surgery, she had what she dreaded — fillings — and then later some dentures. The success of Mrs JI's treatment can be gauged from the fact that I asked her to return in six months' time for a check-up for some advanced dental treatment. She, however, turned up three months later, requesting that I provide her with a crown for her upper incisor.

Although there is nothing unusual in the actual treatment with which Mrs JI was provided, there are differences in the manner in which it was provided when compared to either a general dental practitioner or a hospital dentist. Firstly, Mrs JI was referred to me by one of my colleagues from the LCCC. If this initial step had not occurred then it is unlikely she would have presented herself for treatment until the pain had become unbearable. The fact that Mrs JI was attending the LCCC for physio and OT made it easier for her to receive dental treatment.

> Secondly, Mrs JI was genuinely frightened of anything to
> do with dentistry. Dental treatment then takes much
> longer than to those people who are not apprehensive
> about their dental visits. It would have been very difficult
> to treat Mrs JI in a normal dental surgery because a general
> dental practitioner simply would not have had the time to
> treat her . . . Individuals with Mrs JI's handicap require
> very careful management. A large amount of time is spent
> reassuring, explaining procedures. This continues until the
> person builds up confidence in the dental surgeon and
> comes to terms with their fear of dental procedures. In
> Mrs JI's case this took 12 visits.

This kind of service to elderly people may not be 'unusual in
the actual treatment' offered but it is unusual in being available
as part of what a primary health-care team can provide. The
preliminary figures from the dentist's research suggest that a large
proportion of his patients would be suffering discomfort and even
pain rather than going out to get dental help had they not been
persuaded to accept treatment as a result of their involvement
with the Centre. Not only is it beyond the usual run of dentistry
to seek out those who need dental care and then to approach
them with the kind of patience showed to Mrs JI, but the dentist,
like all the other members of the Centre's therapeutic team, will
make home visits. This is again particularly valuable for older
patients who may be too frail to be able to get out to the Centre.
And domiciliary dentistry is no light matter; the equipment is
quite a weight to get around.

Positive excitement
The dentist's enthusiasm for this kind of pioneering work with
elderly patients suggests another way in which it's safe to be old
at the Lambeth Community Care Centre: the staff neither feel
nor suggest any kind of impatience or weariness with older,
slower patients. It is regrettable but still realistically to be
acknowledged that medicine with old, chronically sick patients
can come to feel like a bit of a bore, a duty, not as exciting as
other kinds of work. Elaine Murphy, Professor of Geriatrics at
Guy's Hospital and author of Dementia and Mental Illness in the
Old, admitted in an interview in The Observer that 'you still hear

junior doctors refer to them [i.e. confused older patients] as "a bit of crumble" — though not while I'm around!'

Dr Murphy also said, 'I do think it's extraordinary when you compare the remarkable high-tech transplants we're doing — and I'm not decrying those developments — with the appalling lack of facilities we provide for elderly people.' The senior nurse at the LCCC has a vision of expanded day-care facilities for older people who need constant attention — open flexible hours after the model of nurseries so that carers can collect their elderly relatives at times to fit in with their work (most current day centres, and indeed the Centre's day unit, shut up shop around mid to late afternoon).

Meantime, the Centre is supporting a great number of elderly people from the area in various ways. It offers an uncategorised kind of care in which a patient's age does not become the most important thing about them. As one of the GPs has written, 'One of the Centre's achievements has been to create excitement and enthusiasm about groups of patients whose care so often has created the reverse. The aim is to fulfil potential, not just to define pathology.'

It's the attitudes implicit in that last sentence and observable within the Centre which fuel the enthusiasm. Not — oh, here's an old person with a mouth full of neglected teeth; I suppose we'll have to take them out. But — here's a person in some pain and need and afraid of the treatment and it's up to me to do all I can to help her to overcome her fear and get her mouth back in as good shape as possible. Not — here's an old person with ulcers, arthritis and some confusion; only to be expected at that age; nothing to be done but dress the ulcers, prescribe Brufen and send them home. But — here's an opportunity to see how much we and this person can do together to maximise their mobility, maybe change their diet, encourage them to become more oriented, more sociable, enjoy as full and independent a life as possible while taking into account their home circumstances. A busy GP could not do all that alone, but a multi-disciplinary team working together in one place can.

There's palpably just as great a sense of achievement at the Centre when a 90-year-old who is longing for her own home is enabled, against the odds, to get back there as there is when an injured teenager walks again. The 'no one's to be given up on' attitude has no age limits.

11 Still Learning

The Centre is a place that trains you to be better informed.
It increases the desire to learn because the benefits are so
obvious.

(Administrator)

When the Centre opened it had in front of it only 18 months of
assured like because that was how long the Inner City
Partnership money would last. A take-over of financial responsibility by the District Health Authority was projected and has
indeed now happened. All the same, there was a very real feeling
around that the Centre had to justify its existence within that 18
months, to show that its philosophy worked in practice. Some
members of the original project group rather regretted the
necessity to move swiftly, wondering if the embodiment of the
Centre's principles wouldn't have been even more firmly
grounded had there been time to move slowly, cautiously,
considering every step in detail. But others, especially those
actively involved in forging the staff team and in particular the
senior nurse, feel that the pressure was in many ways a bonus,
galvanising them into real practical learning when they might
otherwise have stayed at the stage of consideration-of-issues-in-
theory.

On the job

To say that the hard learning comes with practice ('patient
autonomy' not as an idea but as Mr XX with all his unreasonable
demands) is not to denigrate the vital importance of all the prior
thinking that went into the creation of the Centre. Nor is it to

say that thinking isn't a continuing part of the learning process. The place has a reflective spirit about it, but one best employed in inter-active rhythm with experience.

The commitment to continuous learning is there in meetings where all staff have the chance to talk about anything that's bothering them. These include scratchy, difficult meetings when differences can't be resolved and no consensus is reached which means, in turn, more work on the issue because, in the end, everything tends to happen by consensus.

There's hardly one out of the range of meetings that isn't in some way conducive to learning on the job. It sometimes seems to staff, aware of the immediate needs of patients waiting, as if a lot of time goes into meetings. It's also observable, though how closely linked all the meetings remain with learning how best to meet those needs. In a non-hierarchical set-up regular forums are essential — democracy takes time.

There is the occasional and informal, for all the formality of its title, meeting of the education committee, which exists in order to further the education of staff, particularly in relation to one another's jobs. It has, among many other things, arranged for various staff members to explain their own discipline — its theoretical basis and practical application — to other workers who may not be familiar with it. The community link worker, for instance, was able to use such a meeting to reduce the bafflement of her colleagues about what it was she was actually going to do.

There are the regular team meetings at which staff discuss their daily problems; there are the off-the-record senior staff meetings at which an even more frank and full exchange of views can go on. And the monthly audit meetings exist to do exactly what their name says — monitor the Centre's performance, learning from experience and facilitating the application of that learning in future contexts. A look at the agenda of one of the more general audit meetings may give a clearer idea of how the audit operates.

In July 1986 the monthly meeting opened with the intro- duction of new staff. One of the GPs reported that a new project on a local estate, for the treatment of people with a drug dependency problem, was looking for a GP to provide clinical sessions. A brief mention was made of a forthcoming audit meeting about stroke management. SOAP notes were discussed;

staff's anxiety to record anything useful the patient might say about him or herself was identified as a problem since it led to an excess of material making it hard for the GP to find the relevant bits quickly. A plea was made by Centre staff that GPs should write more legibly (some stereotypes are obviously based on reality) and specify who should be carrying out which of their instructions. The shape of referral forms was discussed and therapy staff asked that they should be given more information about the past history of patients and the exact degree of urgency of treatment. Finally, there followed a conversation about the day unit as a whole and the role of day-unit nurses in particular.

This particular audit meeting served mainly as a means of communication. However much work has already gone into sharing between disciplines, there is always scope for more learning. It's not a process that happens once and then is done. It isn't always easy, even now, for a nurse to let a GP know that she has felt angry because that GP has not seemed to be appreciating the seriousness of a situation, for example. Writing in the autumn of 1986, the senior OT was still saying 'The level of public knowledge of occupational therapy is low. This also applies to GPs, district nurses and other professions within the health service.'

Self scrutiny

Even with all the meetings and occasions for sharing, staff were — after about a year — feeling the lack of some kind of stringent, personal evaluation of their own work in order to be able to learn and to develop. Each senior member of staff has a line manager within the District Health Authority to whom he or she is ultimately answerable. But they felt, in the words of an audit meeting report, that their managerial heads were 'remote from the Centre'. So, they evolved their own internal system of evaluation by colleagues. Each member of staff has two designated colleagues with whom work may be discussed in confidence. These colleagues will proffer their honest opinions about the focal person's performance but also enable that person to identify and mull over their own queries about their work and how they've been doing it. This is an entirely voluntary procedure but has been taken up by every Centre-based senior member of staff and found to be useful.

The possibility of this kind of supportive review was also made available (as publicly announced at the meeting in June 1986) to all the GPs contracted to the Centre. So far not one of them has taken up the offer. The reasons are various: some structural, some psychological. One GP said honestly that he had all too shrewd an idea what criticisms might be made of his working practice in relation to the Centre and no desire to hear them coming from other people's lips. Of course for GPs, unlike Centre staff, the Centre is only a part of their working lives, a useful resource but not, by and large, the very heart of their practice. So they have less motivation to volunteer themselves for the discomfort involved in such evaluation. Also, GPs have become used to going their own ways, not being directly answerable to anyone, and it's much harder to move from that position into voluntary submission to formalised close scrutiny than it is for staff who have been accustomed to some kind of supervision. This is not to say that GPs have not learnt a great deal from their closer working with colleagues at the Centre.

Detained evaluation — not just of individual performance but of the work of the Centre as a whole — was written into the project from the beginning. The Inner City Partnership money was given on condition that the Centre was assessed as it developed. This document is a part of that very evaluation — not a health economist's view, not a professional researcher's work, but an attempt to collect and collate the experiences of the Centre's first 18 months, to assemble the perceptions of staff and patients, and to add an outsider's impression of the work so far.

The Centre's research advisory group (aka evaluation group) meets monthly to discuss how research and evaluation should be being carried out. It has collected statistics, concerned itself with the continuous self-auditing of the Centre and of persons and projects within the Centre and has been looking at the major issue of the objective appraisal of the whole thing. The group includes nurses, GPs, therapists, social worker, link worker, dentist, member of the original project team (also ex-Secretary of the CHC) and the Senior Nurse (Research) for the West Lambeth Health Authority who has been particularly helpful with the drafting of a proposal for a research study of the Centre, 'a descriptive study of users' perceptions of the Lambeth

Community Care Centre'. Even as I write arrangements are being set in train to find the right research worker to carry out this project.

The major research project is scheduled to start in 1988 but is far from being the end of the RAG's work. Having set in motion the organisation of the research job, it immediately turned its attention to the progress of the dentist's research work.

In the spring of 1987 the dentist was able to bring to the RAG meeting a report on 'the dental awareness and attitudes' of the GPs associated with the Centre (carried out with a colleague under the auspices of the Department of Community Dental Health at King's College School of Medicine and Dentistry). Of the 32 contracted GPs who'd received questionnaires, 26 had returned them (a response rate of 81%). The study's general conclusion was that, 'although awareness of the cause and prevention of dental caries was good, knowledge of periodontal disease was comparatively limited. There was considerable confusion about National Health Service dental charges and of persons exempt from payment.' This bit of research work is to be used practically to help the dentist to 'plan meaningful education programmes for the doctors'.

Meantime the dentist has been continuing his major study of the dental health of elderly people attending the Centre and was able to offer the RAG some interim figures suggesting that 84 per cent of patients examined were in need of dental treatment, though only 47 per cent actually knew they wanted dental advice, 44 per cent were conscious of there being something wrong with their teeth, mouth or gums and only 16 per cent had visited a dentist within the last year. This work, too, is being carried out not only as a matter of academic interest but as an instrument for the improvement of the Centre's service.

The same RAG meeting which received the dentist's report also looked at different ways of pursuing further research into the effectiveness of the Centre as building. One possible academic study was rejected on the grounds that it would probably not tackle the things of particular interest to the Centre's architects and staff — 'the accessibility of the building to the community . . . the way it is accessible . . . which images affect the way people feel and use it . . . the way spatial arrangements affect users'. The meeting agreed to follow up another academic research proposal which looked as though it might be able to encompass these aspects and also to investigate further how to look at 'the psychology of space and art within the building'. Next on the agenda for a subsequent meeting — a report from the senior physiotherapist on her research.

In order that details of the origins of the Centre, its gestation and birth should be kept on record for reference by anyone interested — perhaps even other people considering starting similar ventures — a small archive group, set up by the RAG, has been busy collecting together written material and photographs relating to the Centre's philosophical basis, its coming into being and its early months.

A teaching opportunity

Side by side with the Centre's self-assessment go the prosaic, day-to-day educative aspects of the Centre's work. A number of the local GPs are trainers; indeed, several of them teach general practice at St Thomas' or King's College Hospitals. Their trainees take on board, at least for consideration, the Centre's attitudes to the practice of medicine. Practically speaking, too, the Centre makes a useful central meeting place and the area's GP trainees get together weekly in the little seminar room under the conservatory.

Nurses new to the Centre are given a two- or three-day induction course which includes time on the ward, in the day unit and out with district nurses. This is necessarily brief and, as so often in the first few days in a new job, can pass in a whirl of impressions. In general, though, new staff are picking up the attitude and ethos of the Centre more and more quickly as that attitude and ethos become more and more second nature to longer-serving staff.

When staff move on that is in itself an educational opportunity, a way of taking a certain approach to patients into other parts of the health service. And when something practised at the Centre — as it might be immediate GP access to physio — is taken up elsewhere, then that should be the occasion not for regret but, as one of the GPs pointed out at an audit meeting, for rejoicing and moving on to add something else new.

In early 1987 the Centre took on a more formal training role by becoming a regular part of the District's nurse-training programme, an opportunity of which they are all very glad since it's another way in which the Centre's ideas and the idea of the Centre may become familiar to a widening circle of nurses. The physiotherapy department has been on the regular training circuit for some time and always has a student on its implement.

The whole business of getting their ideas about primary health care more widely disseminated is one that staff take very seriously. They have, in small teams, gone out to different parts of the country to visit other groups of health professionals, presenting the work of the Centre and answering questions. The day-long presentation by staff of their work at the King's Fund Centre in March 1987 was typical of their 'missionary' activity. That day also reflected in its own organisation some of the things that the Centre values — the multi-disciplinary working shown in demonstrations of quality circle work in action as well as in the variety of staff speaking about the Centre; the emphasis on the equal partnership of the patient shown in a patient's full participation, and that of his wife, in the telling of his own story.

An object lesson

Not all learning, all teaching is straightforward and un-problematic. Nearer to home and perhaps particularly difficult has been the learning to relate tactfully and positively with other bits of the health service. Some aspects of this were well considered before the Centre came into existence and other aspects, it became clear with hindsight, could have been better managed. For instance, because the Centre is geographically within the West Lambeth Health Authority, although it takes its patients from Southwark as well, quite a lot of care went into the relationship with West Lambeth's teaching hospital, St Thomas'. And, while there have no doubt been some occasions of less than perfect communication, evidence suggests that consultants and staff at St Thomas' are well aware of what the Centre is for and see it as a useful additional resource. If there's any problem there, it's that referrals, particularly for post-operative care, are coming almost too fast for adequate preparation, given the Centre's policy of prior visiting and assessment in order to make advance treatment plans.

However, the same amount of forethought did not go into

establishing links with the area's other teaching hospitals. To give just one example of a failure in communication that took time to redeem: a situation arose in which consultant geriatricians from another hospital felt that the Centre, with its short-stay policy, was playing at the interesting bits of care for the elderly only to 'dump' on the geriatricians as soon as it seemed that more difficult issues of long-term care were at issue. This problem was first reported in broad terms to the audit meeting in March 1986. One of the GPs acknowledged that the trigger for the suspicion of the Centre had been his own practice's inappropriate admission of an older person to the Centre without consulting the geriatricians, only to have to call on them urgently for a long-term bed. Two of the Centre's contracted GPs arranged to meet and talk with the geriatricians in general terms about relationships between geriatric services and the Centre. As they reported to the June audit meeting, they found a considerable degree of wariness still present, a fear by the geriatricians that they were going to be used just to get a bed when the Centre couldn't cope. In spite of the GPs' assertions that they were more interested in getting expert advice within a working relationship, the problem created by the initial carelessness of the role and reactions of this other bit of the health service was not instantly repaired by a touch of reassurance.

The lesson that the audit meeting took from this whole discussion was that GPs should, if it looked likely that the advice or resources of a geriatrician or any other kind of specialist would be needed at some point, consult with the person in question from the very beginning, preferably before any admission to the Centre.

Six months or so later it appeared that the working relationship with this particular geriatric unit had become more harmonious and mutually understanding. In the case of Mr N, for example, who was taken off all his medication as a result of the geriatrician's advice, the interaction of consultant and GP and Centre staff operated well in the patient's interest.

To say that this particular working relationship took a year to sort out is not so much to focus on that problem per se as to point out that there is a great deal to be learnt in what is effectively the creation of a new layer of health care. It suggests that special attention should be paid to the existing networks of professional health workers. It is only natural that there will be suspicions among people already working in an area about what a new venture like the LCCC means for them; is it in any sense in competition? Is it going to 'make use' of existing services in a cavalier way, or is it, more subtly, in itself an implied criticism of what is being done already?

Indeed, by its very nature the Centre does raise questions about health care. It would be failing in its own objective if it didn't. So it's not surprising that there should be teething problems in its relationships with other professionals approaching similar problems in a different way. And yet there is no direct contradiction between what teaching hospitals do, what community services do and what the Centre does. It is perfectly possible to fit this intermediate service quite neatly into the existing network — but the rest of the network needs to be kept informed.

In general, though, the District and adjoining Districts have assimilated the Centre well. And in general the necessary learning that staff get from the involvement of consultants at appropriate stages of treatment has worked well, too.

There is one other area in which learning was necessary, one that we come to in the next chapter and that is in the whole relationship between Centre and surrounding community. Again it was an area in which it was easy to assume that all would be well without acually doing very much about it. When the link worker was appointed and began to go out and about, she found that, for all the original community support for the Centre, there also existed quite large areas of ignorance about what it was and did. The moral of the story would seem to be that when it comes to relationships of all kinds around and outside the Centre, as well as within, nothing can be taken for granted. It all needs constant attention.

12 In the Neighbourhood

The real benefits of the Centre are when its lessons spread through the community even when the work and contact with the Centre is completed.

(Local resident/candidate for election to CAG)

The senior nurse met a couple of people whom she knew in the street one day, people who'd been into the Centre for chiropody. They had heard that a young man with a brain tumour had come back from some distance, at the wish of himself and his family, in order that he might die in the Centre (he was living in the area when his illness was first diagnosed and he had been a patient there then). They insisted on giving her some money towards the cost of the transport which had been paid for privately from Centre funds. Such is the increasing network of informal communications between the Centre and its ex-patients and out-patients and patients' friends and relatives.

The Centre's own funds are raised by social events and used at the discretion of Centre staff for such things as taxis, flowers and other gestures — like taking a patient to the cinema — which don't exactly figure large in NHS budgeting. It isn't only the money though that's socially useful; it's also the process of getting it.

When she first started work there the senior nurse was impatient of bazaars, fêtes and the like but has completely changed her mind, having found such occasions to be valuable meeting points for the Centre and people living round it. Indeed, she has even been seen in a wet-suit being bombarded by soaked sponges in this cause. Many of the helpers at fund-raising events have been patients or have had relatives cared for at the Centre.

Money-raising is a useful raison d'être for social events but it isn't the only one. There was, for instance, the imaginative planting picnic, mentioned earlier, when friends of the Centre brought, planted and recorded their offerings to the garden. Just before Christmas there was an open day when coffee and mince-pies were served to visitors all day long. And then there was the Christmas lunch when the screens in the day unit were pulled back to make one large room. Well over 50 people who would otherwise have been alone came in for lunch served by GPs and their families and Centre staff who chose to be there for Christmas Day. The staff has had its own social occasions, too — a Burns Night party in the upper room of the local pub or a Barn Dance in the Centre (with bales of straw borrowed from the local city farm in Vauxhall). And staff and patients and ex-patients were all equal participants in a more recent Caribbean evening of food and drink and dancing.

Personal link

Inevitably, given the Centre's welcoming atmosphere, the more people have been patients there, the greater the number of possibilities for all kinds of contacts with the surrounding area. But the desirability of a genuine relationship with its neighbourhood is one of those things which was planned for by the project team before the Centre even existed. The particular way that the Centre's commitment to being a part of that local community was embodied was in the appointment of a worker whose brief was to 'help link the Centre with the community and the community with the Centre'.

For the bulk of this chapter I am indebted to the community link worker who, after a year in the job, decided that she — and everyone else — could use a full description of what her work had entailed over that year and a comprehensive look at the present state of Centre-community relations. Her report provides the basis for much of what follows.

The job of link worker was felt by the project team, many of them themselves in more traditional health-related jobs, to be one of the more obviously experimental aspects of the Centre's structure. The link worker herself says that, because community workers within the health service are a comparatively recent phenomenon, there is quite a bit of uncertainty around about what to expect of them and also a need for a supportive network (just beginning to develop) for people engaged in health service community work.

An essential preliminary to all her other work was simply getting to know the neighbourhood and its history, the network of small communities within it and all its more formalised groupings from tenants' associations to specific campaigning groups. She also wanted to find out about people's attitudes generally and in relation to health care in particular. By the end of 1986 she had, she felt, a 'fairly detailed knowledge of the local people and the problems they face — collectively as expressed through local "umbrella" organisations and particularly as expressed through local tenants' and residents' associations'.

The 'umbrella' organisations in question are groups like the Association of Waterloo Groups or the North Southwark Community Development Group. To list all the other organisations with which the link worker has had contact may seem a rather dully pedantic thing to do, but the list does cumulatively give a definite flavour of the neighbourhood's multifarious life and suggest the number of potential ways in which the Centre might relate to that life. The organisations are: Walcot Square Residents' Association; Brook Drive Tenants' Association; MOBS SE11 (i.e. Monkton Street, Oakden Street, Brook Drive [Lambeth side], Sullivan Road); Kennington Estates Residents' Association; Renfrew Road Tenants' Association; China Walk Tenants' Association; Princess Street Tenants' Association; Roots and Shoots (a scheme for developing employment skills in young people with learning difficulties); Lambeth Community Advice Team; Asian Advocate Project (existing to help provide a more relevant service to Asian families from two health clinics); Lambeth Crossroads Care Attendant Scheme; Alzheimers Disease Association; St Anne's and All Saints Church Open Door Group (for disabled people in the parish); Waterloo Health Project; Lambeth Inner-City Consultative Group; West Lambeth Health Education Unit; Department of Community Dental Health; Morley College; West Lambeth Community Health Council; British Red Cross Association; Whittington Health Centre; St Luke's Alcohol Rehabilitation

Centre; Al-Anon; Rotherhithe Theatre Workshops; First North Lambeth Brownies; Shelley School (for children with a mental handicap); the neighbouring children's home in Monkton Street; the local police; St Giles Day Centre; Vauxhall City Farm; social services; local clergy.

Since her primary goal at this stage was the acquisition of knowledge, she spent a lot of time listening and learning about problems which ranged from broken paving stones in Brook Drive to the possible effects on the whole Waterloo area of the fixed rail link proposed as part of the Channel Tunnel scheme, from the moving of bus stops in Borough High Street to a general concern about how long it's necessary to wait to get a hospital appointment these days. She also heard a good deal about what local groups are already doing to get effective action in response to their complaints.

Coming and going

The next stage was to encourage individuals and groups to let it be known what they would like of this new resource in their midst, the Community Care Centre. However, people first needed to know about the Centre, and, as noted in the last chapter, the link worker found that there remained — despite all those informal contacts — a surprising degree of ignorance about it. Some thought it was an old people's home, others a hospice or just a small hospital much like any other hospital. In addition to simply explaining the Centre to numbers of local groups, she invited local groups into the Centre so that they could become familiar with it. Three local tenants' associations now regularly hold their meetings there (and through the offices of the community link worker two separate associations from one street have begun to get together).

In her early days at the Centre, the community link worker felt that her colleagues tended at times to treat her as something of a redcoat entertainments manager, turning to her whenever a social event was mooted, passing on all those bits of organisation which didn't quite fit in with anyone else's job. At first she complied, not least because it was a good way to get to know people. Now she feels much freer to say no, I'm not here to run all the jumble sales, better to get volunteers to do that. Where she can, she's been getting local people into the Centre to take over tasks which she herself did at first — she has, for instance, ceded the rather dutiful place she held on the garden committee to someone who lives nearby and who actually knows about gardening.

As well as the bread-and-butter fund-raisers and purely sociable occasions like parties, there've been other events aimed at involving more people with the Centre. Some of these were thought up and arranged by the community link worker, including a pancake week for patients and ex-patients, an Easter bonnet parade by Shelley School pupils, entertainments by the Brownies, afternoons of old-time variety offered by a pensioners theatre group from Rotherhithe and so on. Monthly bingo sessions have been made available in the day unit, entirely at their own suggestion, by a local tenants' association.

Such social activity is — in so far as it offers stimulation to patients and out-patients and strengthens the bonds between community and Centre — a part of the Centre's work, but there is also a way of engaging local people more directly in the day-to-day health-care work of the Centre and that is the volunteers scheme. It's a carefully thought out and organised scheme whereby each of the six volunteers has 'a mutually agreed and defined area of work'. Two work in the garden, two in the day unit, one in the ward and one helps the senior nurse with basic admin jobs like filing. The project has to be kept small, to match the size of the Centre and because it is a serious programme for regular work by people who can both help the Centre and derive some benefit from being there, not just a question of popping in to arrange the flowers. One of the volunteers described this mutually beneficial relationship with the Centre briefly and neatly: 'I come because I like to work and I like to help other people and for the company. I tend the garden, the plants and talk to the patients. Once I did someone's hair'. 'As well as gaining regular individual support from myself,' the link worker writes,

> the volunteers help and support one another. This is achieved through the regular quarterly meetings of the Volunteer Support Group. This group was established out of a need identified by the volunteers to meet together. Within the group everyone has the opportunity to discuss

and exchange ideas and to air any problems or reservations
that they might have encountered.

Although the Centre is not geared to the reception of children
as patients, it welcomes them as friends and visitors and has
always been concerned that there should be a place for them in
any community link work or health education programme. Just
as with adult neighbours, the first steps are being taken by simply
making the Centre available to them, inviting them in to
activities which will encourage them to feel at home there.
There is a relatively newly established Saturday judo club for
children, for instance, which serves the dual function of
familiarising children with the Centre and providing an intro-
duction to a healthy activity.

Going out
Getting people to come to the Centre for one reason or another,
to use it, to begin to feel that it is there *for* them, has been
balanced in the community link worker's approach with a going
out to people and groups in the neighbourhood to see where she
can best offer them her own and the Centre's assistance in what
they are already doing about health care. She has identified two
particular community initiatives where she could be of help, one
the extension of an existing network and the other a brand new
scheme.

The Crossroads Care Attendant Scheme (named for the
erstwhile television soap opera) started 10 years ago with the aim
of helping to relieve the stress of families or individuals
responsible for the care of disabled people (and, exceptionally, of
disabled people living alone). A Lambeth Crossroads Scheme
started as a pilot project in 1984 and during 1986 the community
link worker and the secretary of the local CHC worked with
local clergy, social services, home help organisers, etc, on the
setting up of a North Lambeth branch. 'Meeting regularly in the
Community Care Centre, together we have formed a steering
committee. We have analysed need in the area, found suitable
premises in St Anselm's Church in which to base the scheme;
compiled financial estimates and case studies of potential clients
who would benefit.'

There is no need to reiterate here what that need is. The
chapter about respite care already touched on the great number

of carers in the area and the value to them of some kind of support. The Crossroads scheme was due to start during 1987. What will be interesting to see is quite how it relates to the Centre: whether it will operate separately with the community link worker being, as it were, a resource lent to the scheme by the Centre or whether there will be a genuine working together, an interaction of what the scheme can offer by way of volunteer help at home with the Centre's respite care provisions, a working out of shared concern for the same families.

The other, the new scheme, came out of contacts with the nearby Shelley School for children with a mental handicap. The school, with the link worker, has set up a work-experience programme under which every year a pupil will come to the Centre to work for one day a week. That project got under way in the early summer of 1987.

A major bit of health-education work already on the go is the 'Look After Yourself!' course that the link worker was able to start in April 1987 after she had qualified as a LAY tutor. The course encompasses exercise, relaxation and information and advice about health matters generally. It is hoped that from these initial meetings other courses and groups will follow, with the Centre staff suggesting areas in which health education is desirable and local people suggesting areas in which they wish to be better informed.

The whole present growth of group work within the Centre is conducive to this process of mutual exchange about health care between Centre staff and its clients and potential clients, i.e. anyone in the area. Some groups consist primarily of patients but others, like the group for new mothers, have been instigated by local people who felt the need of mutual support. The link worker's role, and that of those of her colleagues who are involved in groups, is to listen, to accumulate ideas, to pass on to local groups suggestions from Centre staff about what might be useful to the community and to pass on the Centre staff what local people think they need from them. It's an aspect of the work in which many of the Centre's concerns come together and one in which the community link worker's job perhaps most closely approaches the other daily work of the Centre, involving her with colleagues in the facilitating of groups sharing common health problems.

Some of the workshops already run in the day unit, while not directly health-educational, have stimulated patients' interests or self-confidence. At one series of meetings visitors from the horticulture therapy garden in Battersea Park encouraged the development of new perceptions and skills and in another series, Imperial War Museum staff drew on older patients' own experiences of living in the North Lambeth area during the war. Another project through which the Centre may soon become more closely involved in historical study is the proposed Museum of Health at Lambeth Hospital. Through the West Lambeth Community Health Council a steering group was set up to look at the possibility of developing some buildings on the Lambeth Hospital site into a health-care history centre and museum. The London History Workshop Centre was invited to provide leaders for the project, whose aims will be 'to encourage good health, to interpret the history of health care to the public, to help people to understand how to be more healthy and to provide a forum for present-day health issues in a historical context'. It is part of the community link worker's brief to develop connections between this new museum/centre and the Community Care Centre and one way she sees this happening is through the production of the LCCC's own full archive as a contribution.

Bridgework

In order to be a real bridge between Centre and community, the link worker has to put quite a bit of time and energy into simply being a part of both community and Centre. It would be all too easy for the link work to remain rather separate from the other work of the Centre were the link worker to be out and about all the time and not a real part of the Centre team. It has not so far been found appropriate for her to go to those meetings which are concerned with the progress of individual patients, discussions of admission, treatment or discharge, but she is a full participant member of team meetings, senior staff support meetings, audit meetings and the education and arts committees. She does her share of taking the many outside visitors round the Centre, talks with patients and relatives and uses the foyer space for displays of health-care material. She is, of course, a regular member of the research advisory group and the very report on which I've been leaning in this chapter was presented to the RAG in early 1987 as a useful descriptive evaluation of her work to date (and a fairly rare on-the-ground account of what a community worker within the health service actually does).

This everyday aspect of the job — just being a part of the Centre — is one which the link worker says she finds most interesting and challenging. It seems to me that it is also one of the hardest aspects of the work. To go out and meet community groups, to set up schemes and to start health-care courses is relatively straightforward compared with the subtle business of keeping Centre staff aware of what community groups are thinking and fostering partnership from both sides between Centre and community. Within the Centre, when other staff are busy about the immediate needs of patients and you are not, you can feel out on a limb. But then maybe being a link worker is, of its nature, a different, occasionally lonely sort of job. While being a member of the Centre team, you have to be also constantly aware, in a way that other team members may not be, of the community surrounding the Centre; while fully engaged in some community initiative, you have to be constantly aware that your role is to do with the promotion of health in general and the Centre's part in health care in particular.

However, the link worker is no longer the sole formal channel of communication. It has been important that the Centre's commitment to belonging to its neighbourhood be embodied, institutionalised if you like, so that the neighbourhood has a formal way of communicating and, most vital of all, some actual power within the Centre. It had been planned from the beginning that there should be a centre advisory group in which staff and local people would participate on equal terms but the preliminary work of setting it up took longer than expected.

Finally, however, one cold evening in January 1987, about 30 people gathered in the day unit in order to elect the community's representatives to the CAG which consists of seven community members and seven Centre staff. Among the community places, three are reserved for representatives of organisations and six people had been put forward by their groups, mostly local tenants' associations. Eight people were standing for election to the four places kept for individuals with some special experience of or interest in the Centre. All the 14 candidates offered brief written descriptions of themselves; those who were able to be present added spoken comments on why they were standing and, where appropriate, explained the nature of the organisation they were representing. By the end of the evening, the seven successful candidates (age range twenties to sixties) assembled at one end of the room were beginning to turn themselves into a group as they planned their first meeting — at which they would be joined by the seven members of Centre staff (the members of the Centre Management Team plus three elected representatives).

Later in the spring, on a rather milder evening, large numbers of local people responded to an open invitation to the Centre to meet their community representatives and staff over a glass of wine and to talk about their views of what the Centre should be doing. The CAG now meets every two months to discuss the health needs of the area and the role of the Centre. Its purpose is 'to enable local people to have a real say in the planning of the health care they receive'. All substantial issues of policy are referred to it although it does not as a group exert any executive control over the Centre.

In order, however, that it should be an effective body and not just a pleasant talking shop, the chair of the CAG (who must be one of the community representatives) automatically becomes a member of the Centre Management Team, which does have executive power. One of the CAG's early initiatiives, coming primarily from its community members, was the organisation of a study day on AIDS for people from the neighbourhood who wanted to be better informed about the illness.

The first chairperson of the CAG was someone who had no previous medical link with the Centre, had not been a patient or known a patient. She was put forward, with considerable diffidence on her part, by her tenants' association and, when elected chairperson, was equally hesitant about fulfilling that role although doing it excellently. Having thus become involved with the Centre, she has also been to the 'Look After Yourself' sessions on health care there. Being a patient or patient's relative is far from the only way of enjoying the Centre's facilities or contributing to the Centre's work now that the health-education programmes and community — Centre link are really getting into their stride.

The Centre may very well be, in its total combination of

attributes, unique. Its concern for involvement with the local community cannot, however, in all conscience be claimed as particular to the Centre. The West Lambeth Health Authority as a whole is committed to 'community-based definitions of health, community involvement in planning and provision of health services, together with a broad approach to preventing problems and tackling them once they have arisen' (*Towards a Partnership with the Community*, WLHA). The Centre is peculiarly well adapted, though, in size, location and general policy to be an early testing ground of professional — user co-operation in the health service.

Important, and difficult, though the work of the community link worker is and much as she has already accomplished, the mesh of informal contacts between all Centre staff and the Centre's neighbours is also crucial. The deliberate community work with groups and organisations is slowly coming to be all of a piece with the casual, daily, friendly contacts with patients and their families and friends. It is all at a beginning, however, with lots of potential for future change and development.

'In linking the Centre with the community and the community with the Centre,' writes the community link worker, 'what I am aiming for is . . . an integrated approach. Not dual use of the building but rather full participation and quality of involvement from local people and groups in the community.' That can only grow over time, can't possibly spring ready-made from a declaration of intent, but the process is well under way.

13 Where Next?

There should be more like it. They should be everywhere.

(A patient)

Before the Centre came into being, when it was still an idea in the minds of the project group, local support for it, though extensive, was not total. There were people who feared that its creation might somehow lead to a decrease in the quality of health care available to the people of the neighbourhood by offering a second-rate service which allowed the NHS to save on acute medical beds.

If this description has done anything, I hope that it has shown that none of the people who work in or with the Centre, none of its patients, ex-patients and increasing numbers of local friends feel it to be in any way an inferior provision. Rather, they see it as a positive amplification of the health service, adding in a level of general medical care with intensive nursing which is particularly appropriate for some conditions, and which saves only on the unnecessary use of acute medical facilities. It offers, moreover, a genuine invitation to patients to become full partners in their own health care. It is also committed to operating democratically and becoming a genuine part of the community in which it is set.

We've seen some of the difficulties encountered en route to establishing the particular character of the Centre and there are, of course, still some complaints to be found, but they tend to the particular. I cannot, for all my desire to paint a true warts-and-all picture, produce many of them. The garden could do with a greenhouse. The façade looks to some eyes like a petrol station.

There isn't clear enough guidance about exactly what is expected of volunteers (shades of the staff's own difficulties in taking on the full responsibility for their own work). Things of that kind.

General comments about the Centre, on the other hand, tend towards the warmly commendatory.

> As a social services graduate of some 45 years ago, I am delighted that community care has progressed to an extent which would have been unbelievable in my day. I particularly like the friendly and caring attitude of the staff.
>
> (A voluntary helper)

> I recently visited the Centre with my wife for treatment and advice from the physio. The whole atmosphere of the place, including management and staff, was warm and friendly, with caring, sharing surroundings. It was for the first time in the NHS we experienced such an effective and positive relief, which is scarcely found in other health services and is mostly needed by the sick, disabled and the aged. In these days, cuts are more important than lives, thanks to our government.
>
> (Candidate for election to CAG)

> I think the future will prove that this venture which has been pioneered in this area will be copied if finances can be found and it remains my earnest hope that, if we are to strive to have a more caring society, it would be well worth every successive agency which debates its need, to examine its already unique and helpful place which it has developed in the community.
>
> (A GP)

The attitude which informs the Centre's practice — a desire to 'give back' to people, both individually as patients and collectively as communities, a degree of power over their own health care — is relevant not only within the health service but to all forms of social provision, all areas where democratic control and the quality of individual lives matter. It has its cousins within housing, for instance, where developments like Weller Streets Housing Co-operative in Liverpool are giving people the opportunity to be in control of their own environ-ment rather than being at the mercy of either market forces or remote and centralised authoritarian provision.

The Centre does not provide an exact parallel with a housing co-op because health is not an exact parallel with housing. But what the Centre is trying to do is clearly of interest both within and beyond the health service to judge by the number and variety of visitors who have been shown round it during its short life-span. The maintaining of the visitors' book has somewhat given way under the pressure but surviving records show that professional health workers visiting the Centre have included staff from assorted London hospitals, non-contracted GPs, GP trainees, medical students, health visitors, midwives, health authority staff, OTs, CHC members, dental students, health educationists, visitors from the Royal College of Nursing and from a hospital for 'incurables'.

Those visitors who are not working directly in the health service include at least two distinct groups. One is what you might call professional observers — TV crews, journalists, people who've decided that it's worth taking in what's happening at the Centre in order to communicate it to other people. The other is people who feel that the general approach of the Centre may be relevant to their own lives or work and these include local residents and community groups, care attendant scheme workers, clergy, architectural students, planners, consumer advisers, charitable workers (from e.g. Age Concern and the Alzheimers Disease Association), day-centre staff and visitors from educational establishments ranging from local sixth-forms to the Royal Academy of Music.

They've come from all over the country, from Salisbury and York, from Liverpool and Edinburgh. But they've also come from all over the world and records show contacts with people from Germany, Sweden, Hungary, Holland, Australia, America, South Africa, Gaza. And this is only some from among the visits recorded. Every time I was in the Centre, it seemed, I came across the administrator or link worker or social worker patiently showing round either a solitary guest or a little troupe of watching, question-asking visitors. It takes time but staff do it because they believe what they're up to is valuable enough to share, to pass on. They all hope that other people are going to

think about the possibility of Community Care Centres elsewhere or at least take up some of the ideas implicit in the
Centre's work — ideas in particular about intermediate health
care and in general about empowering people to take control of
their own lives.

Also published in the **Community Action** series:

Allan McNaught
Health Action and Ethnic Minorities
Grassroots Initiatives : A Selection from New Society

Barbara Saunders
Homeless Young People in Britain: The Contribution of the
Voluntary Sector

Joan Davidson
How Green is Your City? Pioneering Approaches to
Environmental Action

Peter Ashby
Trade Unions and the Community: Working for Jobs

Charmian Kenner
Whose Needs Count? Community Action for Health